To Bill Murphy

with best wishes

Sincerely

Gregory Clark

FISHING

with

GREGORY CLARK

OPTIMUM PUBLISHING COMPANY LIMITED
Montreal

Introduction

This new collection of stories concentrates on Gregory Clark's favourite subject—fishing. As Greg's foreword announces, "fishing is the least objectionable way of doing nothing." Clark devotees will immediately recognize how much of this amazing author's philosophy is tied to his favourite pastime.

With the exception of 3 classic stories reprinted from "Which We Did" (1936), none of the other stories have ever appeared in book form although nostalgically, you may remember reading them in Greg's column in *Weekend Magazine*.

So the book you hold in your hands is a fascinating record of fishing adventures and fishing companions told as only Canada's venerable, master story teller can.

Ernest Hemingway, Greg's friend and sometime fishing companion, wrote the following about the puzzling little man with whom he worked at *The Toronto Star:*

> "He loves his wife and his baby. He loves hunting and fishing and fishing tackle . . . He also loves to think. He thinks very well but he never strains himself. He likes it about Canada, too . . . Greg is very romantic. But I can never understand all the way inside of him because he is romantic. I am romantic too and that is the trouble. You cannot dismiss him or classify him because he is always acting and you cannot tell how much of it is acting. He also acts inside himself. He is an officer and a gentleman . . . He writes the best of anyone on the paper. I have known him a long time but I do not know much about him."

It is difficult to add to Hemingway's words.

The Editors
September, 1975

Fishing With Gregory Clark
by Gregory Clark

Copyright © 1975 by Optimum Publishing Company
Limited

Published by Optimum Publishing Company Limited,
245 rue St. Jacques, Montreal, Quebec H2Y 1M6
Michael S. Baxendale, Director

Trade Distribution in Canada
Prentice-Hall of Canada, Ltd.,
1870 Birchmount Road, Scarborough, Ontario

The copyright material on page 3 and on the dustjacket is
reprinted by permission of Charles Scribner's Sons from
Ernest Hemingway: A Life Story by Carlos Baker.
Copyright © 1969 Carlos Baker

Photographs—Weekend Magazine

ISBN   0-88890-033-3

Cover—by Jack Tremblay
Design—Max Newton

Printed and bound in Canada

Contents

Foreword

Fishing is the least objectionable way of doing nothing. If you try to do nothing by sitting on the back steps, your wife is almost certain to suggest that you repair the screen door. If you attempt to do nothing by sitting in a deck chair at the bottom of the yard, behind the spiraea bush, a neighbor is sure to suggest that you help him straighten up the mutual fence.

But fishing is highly respectable. It is manly. It is outdoorsy.

Suppose you had the habit, all through spring, summer and autumn, of just quietly disappearing for the weekend, abandoning your wife and children, while you went up to some backwoods village and lay in bed from Friday night to Sunday afternoon, what would the neighbors think? What would your wife and her mother say?

But if you have the habit of simply beating it Friday, at 5 p.m., with a decent display of hip rubber boots, fishing rods and tackle boxes as you load them into your car, all is well. You are a fisherman.

The neighbors understand. Your wife merely says men are queer. And her mother says good riddance.

But there is far more to fishing than doing nothing in a publicly-approved fashion. Fishing is the only manly pastime in which you can form and entertain a high opinion of yourself without having to deliver the goods.

It is the only sport in which you can build a reputation founded entirely on your own say-so.

Golf is different. You usually need a partner. And you must keep score, more or less. If you are a dub, even you know it.

Tennis, bowling and all team sports are the same. You've got to be good. You can't deceive others, and it is idle to attempt to deceive yourself.

But fishing is unique. If you come home without any fish, you have only to say that you are so dedicated to sporting methods and sporting tackle that you could not do as other men do, and resort to the net, the spear and dynamite. Your family and friends respect you. You are a sportsman.

If you make the mistake of going away with a gang which includes some fish hogs who really can catch fish, you need not be found out. Fishing at its best is a solitary vice, as Lord Byron said. The best anglers fish alone. When you come in at the end of the day and find your companions flapping a whale of a catch out on the cabin veranda, all you have to do is adopt an air of weary content, a sort of joyous exhaustion, and declare that you have never had such a day. You must have taken 30 or 35 fish, three of them at least two-pounders. But you didn't keep any. You don't believe in killing a lot of fish. It is the sport you are after.

This, if done skilfully, abashes your companions and makes them feel like a bunch of fishmongers.

If someone has a monster fish, a bigger one got away from you.

To support this attitude, you must spend a little money on fine and sporty tackle. When you have done this, you begin to believe yourself. You have reached the stage in which, indeed, your failure to latch on to a bag of fish is due to your delicate tackle, you high sporting ethics.

Which become so high, in fact, that you can lie in bed, from Friday night to Sunday noon, in that backwoods hotel, without a qualm. Fishing, for a fact, is unique.

Gregory Clark

The Code

I think, I think," said my friend Bill Milne excitedly over the telephone, "I can wangle you an invitation to the Skittywabo for the opening of the trout season!"

My hair stood on end.

"Wonderful!" I yelled.

The Skittywabo Fish and Game Club, I might tell you, is the last word, the acme, the *ne plus ultra,* the paragon—hell, it's the greatest trout-fishing club in the world.

It has 17 private lakes, five miles of the most beautiful tumbling stream, its membership is so exclusive and so disdainful of money you couldn't get a membership in it if you had a million dollars.

"Bill!" I cried. "How can you find out? When will you know? How do I . . . ?"

"Tonight," replied Bill. "I am to telephone long distance to Angus MacKillup after dinner. I told him this afternoon you would give your shirt for an invitation. And he said he would get in touch with the club secretary and see how many guests had already been . . ."

"Wow!" I shouted. "Bill, what time are you to call him?"

"After supper. I'll give him a ring about 8 o'clock. Then I'll call you right away."

My heart suddenly sank.

"Bill!" I groaned. "This is awful. Awful!"

"What's the matter?" protested he.

"It's AWFUL, Bill," I moaned. "I just this minute remembered that Harry Parrish is calling me after supper. Do you know what?"

"What?" said Bill.

"He's seeing if he can take me with him to the Cranberry Lake Fishing Club for the opening!"

"No!"

"It's a fact," I declared. "He telephoned me only this morning and asked me if I could go with him if there was a vacancy."

"Cranberry Lake's a pretty good club," said Bill.

"Aw, but not in the class of the Skittywabo!" I cried. "Parrish was going to see THEIR secretary this afternoon and find out if there is room for one more guest for the opening. And he is phoning me after supper. At 8 o'clock!"

"Well," considered Bill, "let's see. You're fixed up, one way or the other. If Parrish calls you first, stall him some way until you hear from me."

"You can't stall on a thing like this!" I scoffed indignantly. "Holy smoke! Two of the most exclusive trout clubs in the country!"

"Well, maybe I could call MacKillup," suggested Bill, "and tell him you are dated up . . ."

"No, no, NO!" I countered. "Couldn't you call MacKillup before dinner? See if he's going to ask me?"

"You can't appear too eager," explained Bill, "with these big shots like Angus."

Boy-o-boy! The Skittywabo. Or the Cranberry Lake. The dream of a lifetime.

"I've got it!" exclaimed Bill over the phone. "We'll work on a code. Who's at your house tonight?"

"Just my wife," I said. "We're alone tonight."

"Good!" said Bill. "Now get this. Don't you answer the telephone. Do you hear me? From 6 o'clock on, don't you answer your phone unless you get this series of rings, which will be me, see? I'll call

10

your number and let it ring four times. Then I'll hang up. Then I'll dial you a second time, right away, and let it ring twice, and then I'll hang up. Four: then a pause. Two: then another pause, see? And the next time it rings, it'll be me!"

"Aha!" I exulted. "Four rings and a pause. Two rings and a pause. Then you ring again, and it's you."

"Code, see?" said Bill. "So, if Parrish calls you, or anybody else, just let it ring, as if you were out. He'll call you later. Meanwhile, I give you the code ring and give you the word from MacKillup."

Grand.

Bill's a wonderful guy. Ingenious.

My wife and I had supper early, and I explained the setup to her and warned her not to answer the phone. Leave it all to me.

At 7:20 p.m. the phone rang 11 times and then gave up.

"Maybe it was Hazel," said my wife, "for me."

"Parrish, I bet," I responded.

At 8:05 p.m., it rang again, 14 rings. Then gave up.

"Parrish, sure as fate," I calculated.

At 8:25 p.m. the phone rang. I leaped and stood ready.

It rang four times and then abruptly stopped.

"Bill!" I announced.

Then it rang twice.

And stopped.

I had my hand ready at the receiver, and on the next very first ring, I lifted it and sang out heartily: "HELL-ooooo!"

It was Harry Parrish!

"Your phone must be out of order," said he. "No answer for a while, and then a busy signal. Say! It's

11

all O.K. for Cranberry Lake!"

He spoke triumphantly.

"Uh . . . " I said. "Well . . . er . . . ah! Harry!"

"What did you say?" asked Parrish, a little astonished.

I did not know what to say. How to stall. It had caught me so unawares. That code.

"Harry," I spluttered. "I can't be sure whether I can go. Something has turned up at the office. Could I have a day or so . . . ?"

"Golly, no," said Parrish. "Greg, I had to move heaven and earth to wangle you in as a guest for the opening. And I promised the secretary I would call him right back tonight to confirm . . . "

Well, I could hear a little clicking sound in the receiver, and knew it was Bill trying to get me.

So I told Parrish most regretfully that, since this thing that had blown up at the office, there was a chance I might have to drop out, perhaps it would be better, all things considered . . .

I thanked him from the bottom of my heart. To have to pass up an invitation to the Cranberry Lake Club!

We hung up.

The phone rang four. It rang two.

"Bill?"

"Sorry, old boy," said Bill, very crestfallen. "Angus MacKillup moved heaven and earth, but the secretary said the Skittywabo was already two guests over the allowance already, for the opening . . . "

Codes?

Yah.

The Bargain

Old Dandy Daniels cannot pass up a bargain.

How you can live to 80 years of age—give or take five years, and old Dandy won't tell—without learning that there is no such thing as a bargain, I will never know.

"Dandy," I protested, "the thing is damaged! It's busted. Look, the hinge is all twisted . . . "

"Three bucks!" hissed Dandy. "Regular, $8.95!"

Dandy had hold of this fishing-tackle box.

"Aw, Dandy!" I wailed.

Every year, about this time of spring, I have to take Dandy on a grand tour of the fishing-tackle and sporting-goods stores. All the fishing tackle the old boy will use for the rest of his life you could put in your hat.

We go downtown for lunch together, to a restaurant that is not famous, but where they have a real fish cook. And we eat jumbo finnan haddie, grilled, with scalloped potatoes and stewed tomatoes; or fillets of New York flounder, poached in white wine,(Dandy smuggles the half-bottle of white wine, a Chablis, in, in his overcoat pocket); or the tail ends of Lake Superior lake trout, broiled, with shoe-string potatoes, and broccoli singed in butter.

However, after lunch, I then take old Dandy on this grand tour of the tackle shops and sporting-goods stores, where we inspect all the new merchandise, swish the very latest glass rods, fondle all the brand-new plugs, lures, spoons and 100-percent-guaranteed fish-getter, argue with the proprietors, quarrel with the clerks, get into all sorts of disputes with other customers, whom Dandy tries to talk out of buying what they have their hearts set on.

"Three bucks!" insisted Dandy, clutching the big khaki tin tackle box.

"Dandy, old friend," I reasoned, though I knew it was hopeless, "if it could be repaired, they wouldn't let it go for three bucks."

"I know the very fella," said Dandy, "who can fix it for 50 cents!"

"What do you want," I demanded, mistakenly, "with a tackle box?"

That did it. Dandy had a clerk wrap it up, paid his $3, and I had to carry the clumsy parcel to the next five tackle shops. Dandy hasn't carried any parcels for the last 15 years.

When we went to the parking lot for my car, Dandy said:

"We'll just go home around by this fella, where I can leave the box."

"Where is it?"

"Willowdale," said Dandy.

Willowdale is a suburb, about 10 miles west, roughly 20 miles out of our way home, there and back. During the home-going traffic crush.

"He has fixed a lot of things for me," explained Dandy.

"Let's go out there some day in the morning," I suggested.

"Let's," suggested Dandy, "do it on the way home."

He had the tackle box on his knees.

At Bathurst and St. Clair, where I was the last to cross when the lights changed, I was hit on the tail by an insurance man who claimed the lights HAD changed, and there is no use arguing with an insurance man, especially when he is driving a company car. At $100 deductible, though it was only $17 for the tail light and a crumpled bit of fender, I had to pay the $17 (later).

We got to Willowdale, and Dandy directed me to the exact spot where this fella lives who was going to repair the tackle box for 50 cents.

"Why," cried Dandy, "he had a shack right here."

"A shack?" I checked.

For we were in a street filled with lovely little new housing-development bungalows.

We drove back around to the corner, where I got out and inquired at the new drug store, in which the plaster wasn't quite dry, for the whereabouts of a fella, whose name Dandy did not know, who had a little sort of handyman shack there, before the housing development.

"A fine thing!" said old Dandy, when I returned to the car. "A genius like him. And nobody can remember him."

"Maybe now," I suggested, it being 6 p.m., "you can find somebody else who can repair the tackle box for 75 cents, eh?"

"O.K., O.K.," responded Dandy bitterly.

So I took one of the big cross-town highways that would get us home somewhere before 7 p.m.

"Step on it," said Dandy, whose stomach was rumbling. He likes his meals on time. "There will be no cops out at this time of night. They'll all be home for supper."

So I stepped on it; but there was one cop; probably, as Dandy figured it, a bachelor, or else a guy with ulcers.

He ran alongside and pushed us over to the shoulder.

The ticket he gave me was for $10.

"Hortense," said Dandy, "will be furious. She sets

dinner at six."

Hortense is the housekeeper he has had for the last 40 years in their neat, tidy, bargain-filled little bachelor menage.

But I stuck to 30 miles an hour, and it was 7:20 p.m. when I delivered Dandy at his door.

He did not invite me in for supper.

"Hortense!" he explained.

And he tip-toed up the steps with the tackle box in his arms.

To the best of my information, with Hortense as my chief source, it cost Dandy $1.85 to take a taxi down to the tackle shop where he tried to return the tackle box, only to find that they did not accept bargain goods in return. It cost him another $3.15, after careful study of the yellow pages of the telephone book, to call by taxi on two other repair shops, where they wanted $5 and $6.50 to repair the hinges and push out the dents on the tackle box. It cost him $1.55 for a taxi to get him home. With the tackle box.

He still has the tackle box. And the way I figure it, it cost $3, plus the $17 for my bent fender, plus $10 for the speeding ticket, plus $1.85, plus $3.15, plus $1.55 in taxis—total, $36.55.

When I suggested this to Dandy, do you know what he said?

"You think you're pretty smart, don't you?"

But of course, next spring, that is, 1958, if Dandy is still alive, we'll be going on our grand tour of the tackle shops.

And we'll start off with, say, fillets of pickerel, grilled, with no vegetables, but only a tossed green spring salad.

Or maybe Boston scrod, this little restaurant I speak of, knowing its way around, with parsley boiled potatoes.

Or let us say, smelts!

Jumbo smelts, with sliced cucumber, and a great sprig of parsley not to look at, but to EAT.

The Opening

The first day of trout fishing is, of course, by long odds the best. There is a ceremonial, a festival air in it.

W. C. Milne and I walked down the sloping village street like pilgrims marching the last hundred yards to their shrine.

We held our fly rods before us, all strung up and ready, the way bishops carry their croziers.

"What a morning!" muttered Milne.

It was 6 a.m. Robins, orioles and purple martins were chirping, singing, carolling. Not a soul of the village was up or about. We had the world to ourselves. The sun had not yet cleared the tops of the village trees, and everything was bathed in that luminous glow that occurs at no other time of day.

Pacing slower, we reached the bridge.

"Once more, Bill!" I said, holding out my hand.

We clasped hands. Once more we had arrived for the opening of the trout season at our beloved bridge. Under it, quiet, smooth and wide as a country road, ran the little Mad River, one of the greatest trout streams we had encountered in all our searching. We had now fished it 10 seasons, and knew every twist and turn of it, every pool, every sunken log, every tree and sheltering shrub along its banks, as we knew the shape and feel of

17

our own hands.

We leaned on the bridge rails to stare down in the streaming, shadowed water, clear as crystal. We gazed upstream, the direction in which we had to fish, since our lease ran from the bridge upstream to the far end of the farm.

"Well?" said Milne. "Shall we toss?"

This was an established part of the ritual. Whoever won the toss had the choice of starting to fish right here, at the Bridge Pool, and would fish his way, slowly, pool by pool, up to what was called the Low Bend, which was half-way up our stretch of the river.

The loser had to walk through the fields, skirting the stream, to the Low Bend, and start there, fishing up to the limits of our lease.

This was an ideal division of the fishing, because it gave winner and loser each one magnificent pool—the Guest Pool on the lower half, and Sing's Spring on the upper half. These two sites afforded the greatest fishing for miles and miles around.

Milne tossed a quarter. I won.

"I'll start here, Bill," I announced. For I had already detected a couple of bulges and a smart splash or two in the Bridge Pool. The trout were on the rise!

"Right-o!" said Milne. "Tight lines!"

"Long may your reel screech!" I gave him back.

Off the Bridge and into the fields wet with dew he headed.

I was in no hurry. It is a great mistake to rush at what you love. It is more seemly to come reverently. I leaned on the bridge rail and watched Milne striding through the tall grass until he disappeared around the trees of the bend that hides the Guest Pool, my pool, from sight.

Ah, dear old Bill Milne! We had known each other longer than either of us could remember. We had been children together, then students, then soldiers, then companions, year after year, on fishing trips too countless to be estimated.

That is the great thing about fishing. It makes for longer, more continuous companionship than any other sport or pastime. Golfers play with far too many partners over the years to establish the kind of narrow communion anglers develop. What other sport allows such opportunity to know your companion in all his virtues?

When Milne disappeared around the bend, I picked up my fly rod and prepared to make a few casts right off the bridge. There doubtless would be a couple of good ones, this early in the season, hiding in the shelter of the bridge itself.

I flicked off some line and was about to lay the fly on the water when a thought struck me.

I stared up the field where Milne had vanished.

I wonder, I said to myself, *would that son of a gun have the nerve to stop at my Guest Pool on his way past?*

Aw, perish the thought!

So I waved the rod again and was just extending the line to a nice distance to drop the fly at the far end of the Bridge Pool when I reeled in.

I'll bet you, I said to myself, *that right this MINUTE, that son of a gun is kneeling there, beside that little bush at the Guest Pool, and is preparing to take MY trout maybe a 15-inchser, maybe a TWO-POUNDER . . . !*

I carried my rod nimbly off the bridge and hid it hastily against a tree. Following Milne's trail in the wet grass, I hurried for the bend.

Before reaching it, I slowed down and peered ahead through the young-leafed trees. I stooped and rounded the bend behind some willow brush.

There, crouching low, staring intently at the lovely surface of the Guest Pool was my life-long pal.

Maybe, I thought, *he is just LOOKING.*

In the shelter of the willows, I crept closer.

Milne cautiously shifted the strap of his creel off his shoulder and laid the basket aside. Kneeling, he raised his rod and waved it until the line was extended in the air 40, 45, 50 feet.

Smooth, silent, silky, the line straightened, the gut leader and the fly dropped imperceptibly on the water where it hurried at the entrance to the Guest Pool.

I held my breath. So, of course, did Milne. The fly came down and entered the pool.

There was a bulge, a humping of the water.

Milne struck.

And when he rose instantly to his feet, his rod was curved in the glorious pulsing arc that spells a big trout.

It was a spectacular battle. Of course, Milne was so occupied, his attention so riveted in the water, that I was able, by using infantry tactics, to make short rushes, from bush to bush, until I was directly behind him at a distance of about 40 feet.

There in the dewy grass, I sat down and rested my elbows on my knees in the spectator attitude.

Milne fought the trout, a 16-incher, fat, close to a pound and 10 ounces, until it was on its side.

Proudly, he waded out and slid the landing net under it.

Proudly, this being the first trout on the first day of the ceremonial opening of this glorious occasion, he waded ashore.

And there, sitting in the grass 40 feet away, was I.

It is of such moments as this that the compelling,

mysterious and indestructible companionship of fishing really consists.

Sly Fishing

Owing to a slight touch of lumbago, Mr. P. J. McGarvey was unable to accompany us to his summer cottage for the weekend.

So he gave us the keys.

"Now, remember," he warned us, "Right after breakfast, go and sit on the veranda, all ready to go. And when Old Man White comes down from HIS cottage, to HIS dock, get set. And when he takes off in his boat, the minute his back is turned, get crackin' and follow him."

"Won't he catch on we're following him?" I asked.

"Certainly not," said Mr. McGarvey. "He's driving his outboard. He's got his back to you. He never looks back."

"Then?" asked Milne.

"Just keep him in sight," said Mr. McGarvey. "When he rounds an island or a point, speed up so you don't lose him. Then, finally, you'll come round a corner, and there he'll be. Anchored. And fishing."

"And?" said Herriot.

"Well, hell," said old Mr. McGarvey, as he twinged with a touch of lumbago, "what more do you want? Where he's fishing, that's where the fish are. Run right close to him, anchor and start fishing."

"Is he that good?" I asked.

"Is he that GOOD!" cried Mr. McGarvey. "Where do you think I got all those snapshots of the trout I showed you? From following Old Man White the past 25 years. That's where."

"Well, then . . . " said Milne, Herriot and I, wishing dear old Mr. McGarvey a speedy recovery from his lumbago, and expressing our deepest thanks for letting us have the use of his cottage the weekend.

Mr. McGarvey used to stop us on the street and pull out of his pocket the latest snapshots, summer, autumn, winter, showing us the most wonderful strings of beautiful trout, a pound, pound and a half, two pounds.

"From up at my place." Mr. McGarvey would say.

This was very strange to us. Because, between you and us, we had made at least a dozen trips, without Mr. McGarvey's knowledge, to his famous lake. And never, never, did we get more than three or four little tiddlers, eight- and nine-inch trout. And we had to fish them with worms.

"All on the fly," Mr. McGarvey would say, taking back his snapshots reverently.

Finally, Mr. McGarvey invited us to spend the weekend with him.

Then the lumbago.

"Boys," he said, when we learned the bad news and drove up to his house to get the keys. "Boys, I'm going to let you into a little secret. There's only the one real fisherman up at my lake. He's an old cuss by the name of White. He's the only successful angler in the whole place. And I've got to confess I've been following the old boy, surreptitiously, all these years. Yes, I confess it. Surreptitiously. I wait until I see him start off fishing. Then I follow him. I hide around the point until he quits. Then I move in. THAT is how I made all those catches I've showed you."

Old Mr. McGarvey was quite broken up with his confession plus the lumbago.

"So, boys," he said, "do as I tell you. Only, since you'll only have a day and a half to fish, don't hide around the corner. Move right in alongside him. It's the ONLY way to get fish at Lake Awiskwijing."

We arrived at Mr. McGarvey's cottage after dark, had a good night's sleep in his comfortable beds, and were up and had breakfast over by 7 a.m. Saturday.

Old Man White's cottage was directly opposite, the only one on a small island.

We had seen signs of activity ever since we had been up. We caught glimpses of Old Man White from time to time, throwing dishwater out the back door, collecting an armful of stove wood from the woodpile. He did not appear to be in a hurry.

When, with our tackle all stacked ready on the veranda, we took our place, we could see Old Man White come and sit on his veranda.

"He doesn't look so old." said Milne.

"Well," said Herriot, "Mr. McGarvey has reached the age when he thinks everybody is old. He probably calls us old."

We sat from shortly after 7 until well past 8 with no sign of Old Man White taking to his boat.

Milne went out behind and split some kindling for Mr. McGarvey's kindling pile. I tied up three or four fresh 7½-foot leaders, stout nylon, suitable for holding two-pounders. Herriot went inside and made a fresh pot of coffee.

When 9 o'clock came, with Old Man White still sitting in his rocking chair on the veranda across the 200-yard channel, we began to get restless.

By 9:30, we said if he didn't get going, we'd go at 10, and to heck with him.

At 10 we carried our rods and haversacks down to Mr. McGarvey's outboard.

Down the rocks across the channel came Old Man White.

"Psst!" we warned one another.

So we sat on the dock. Old Man White sat on his. Fifteen minutes passed.

"Look," said Herriot. "To heck with it."

So we got in our boat. Old Man White got in his. We yanked the engine. He yanked his.

Slowly we started east toward an attractive cluster of small islands, a likely-looking habitat.

Slowly Old Man White followed.

We stopped over some shoals and started to fish.

Old Man White stopped 100 yards short of us and started to fish too.

After 20 minutes of nothing, Milne said:

"This is ridiculous."

So we yanked the motor and left at high speed for the far side of the lake, a mile off, where some cliffs came down to the water.

And a few hundred yards behind us came Old Man White, full speed.

We fished along the cliffs. Old Man White fished along the cliffs 100 yards in our wake.

Just before noon, when Milne was starting to unlatch the lunch hamper to see what was in store, Herriot, who was at the steering handle of the outboard, turned us back toward Old Man White.

"Let's be frank," he said, "and ASK the old boy where's the best place."

We ran close alongside. Old Man White was quite a pleasant-looking chap in his fifties, I should say.

"Mr. White?" I sang out.

24

"No, I'm not Mr. White," sang back the stranger, "He just lent me his cottage for the weekend."

"Oh," said we.

"Maybe you think it's funny," said the stranger, "me following you everywhere, Mr. McGarvey. But Mr. White told me to be sure and follow you, because you knew where all the good fishing spots were. Which is Mr. McGarvey?"

"Well," said Herriot. "Mr. McGarvey isn't with us. He lent us HIS cottage for the weekend."

"Oh," said he.

So we joined forces and fished at random around Lake Awiskwijing without any success whatever.

And when we went back in at dusk for supper, and Mr. McGarvey's local housekeeper and tidy-upper came around to see how we were doing, we told her about the two old gentlemen tipping their guests off to follow one another.

"Oh, them two," said she. "They've been following each other secretly around this lake for 30 years. They each think the other is the greatest fisherman in the world."

Which isn't a BIT like ordinary fishermen.

Maybe that is why they are lucky.

The Deposit

Joe Bell phoned. "Hey, Greg," he said, "haven't I heard you talking about a lake called Riley's Lake?"

"You sure have," I replied, "I fished there every spring until about 1950."

"What's it like?" asked Joe.

"Well, there's no fish in it now, if that's what you

25

mean," I said. "Fished out."

"Any cottages?" inquired Joe.

"Too many," I said. "That's the trouble. When I first started going there, oh, 30 years back, there were only a dozen cottages or so. But now there's a hundred, all looking in each other's back doors, and the lake is whizzing with outboards and water skiers."

Joe Bell groaned.

"I'm in a mess," he said. "I've just paid down $100 on a cottage there. Read an ad, and some fellow at Williams' Mills . . . "

"That's the village, about four miles away," I said.

"This fellow sent me some color slides of this cottage," said Joe, "so my wife and I took it in desperation—$400 for July and August. We left it pretty late to try and rent a place. And the day after I sent the $100 deposit, darned if my wife's cousin, Wesley, didn't write us offering us HIS cottage, free."

"Aw," said I.

"Free," said Joe. "And it's a swell little place. We've often been there. Wesley and his wife have to be at Minneapolis all summer on a course he's got to take in electronics."

"Can't you write the guy at Williams' Mills?" I suggested.

"I was thinking of running up to see him this weekend," said Joe. "That might be better than writing. And I thought you . . . "

"Sure, Joe," I agreed. "I'd love to go. You drive, eh?"

It would be fun to see Riley's Lake after 10 years.

As we turned off the highway on the gravel road to Williams' Mills, Joe showed me the receipt he had from a Mr. Markoff, the agent.

One hundred dollars.

"I don't recall any Mr. Markoff in my time," I said.

The gas-pump boys in the village directed us to Mr. Markoff's house.

"I'm Mrs. Markoff," said the pleasant lady who answered the door. "My husband is out. I wouldn't be surprised if he isn't down at the cottages right now. We've got several down at the lake."

She explained that we drove on four miles to a new plantation of little pines the government had put in, turn right down to the lake, and the fourth cottage in would be the one. There was a board marked "Markoff No. 3" on a tree.

We drove down to the lake. If there had been 100 cottages on it the last time I saw it, there must be 200 now. They were cheek by jowl. They were even one behind the other.

We parked at "Markoff No. 3," and saw a big green car drawn up beside the cottage.

When we walked in the path, there was a man sitting on the veranda steps.

"Mr. Markoff?" said Joe Bell.

The gentleman stood up. A thin, parchmenty gentleman with a thin neck, and his hat teetered on the top of his head.

"I'm Bell," said Joe. "Joe Bell. I sent you the $100 deposit on this cottage? I've come up to see about the lease."

The gentleman looked at us stonily.

"Mr. Bell," he said, "I'm terribly sorry. But there has been a mix-up."

"A mix-up?" said Joe.

"I'm afraid," he said, "I'll have to repay you your $100 deposit."

"Aw!" said Joe, trying not to sound too relieved.

"Yes," said Mr. Markoff. "It seems another applicant had already closed the deal, and I had got confused . . ."

He had his wallet out and was poking in it.

"Well," said Joe, looking as injured as should be expected of him. "It's pretty darn' late in the season. If this is the way you do business . . ."

Mr. Markoff counted out five $20 bills and held them out.

Joe took them promptly and pocketed them.

"I'm extremely sorry," said Mr. Markoff, stiffly.

"Good day," said Joe, equally stiff.

A lady appeared around the end of the cottage with a handful of wild flowers.

"Ah," said Mr. Markoff. "My wife, Mrs. Markoff."

We looked at her with surprise. But in no more surprise than hers.

"How do you do?" she said, looking at her husband.

Joe and I walked up the path briskly.

"That dump," said Joe, as we got into the car, "looks no more like the color slides he sent. They must have been taken 20 years ago."

We drove back out to the gravel.

"I don't THINK," said Joe, patting his wallet pocket with the $100 in it, "that THAT was Mr. Markoff at all."

"Not Markoff?" said I.

"We're going to park in Williams' Mills a little while," said Joe, excitedly, putting on speed.

Joe drew his car off to one side about 100 yards down the village street from Markoff's house.

In less than 10 minutes, the green car we had seen at the cottage pulled up in front of Markoff's and Mr. Markoff and his wife got out and rapped on the door.

"Aha!" said Joe. "Rapping on his own door?"

They were in for about half an hour, came out, said goodbye to a short, fat gentleman in his shirt sleeves, and drove off.

Joe turned and drove over.

"Mr. Markoff?" said Joe, when the short man appeared at the door. "I'm Joe Bell. I sent you $100 deposit on the . . ."

"Why, hello!" said the real Mr. Markoff. "It's not two minutes since the gentleman you met down at the cottage . . ."

Joe waved Mr. Markoff into the house, and we followed.

"THAT gentleman," said Joe, "said HE was Mr. Markoff!"

"HE?" said Markoff.

"He told me," said Joe, "and here's my witness, that there had been a mix-up, and he was forced to pay me back my deposit!"

"Why, for goodness' sakes," said Mr. Markoff, "he told ME you had willingly surrendered your option and he paid YOU the deposit!"

"Mr. Markoff," said Joe, drawing the papers from his pocket. "I have here your receipt for $100 and your letter advising me to come and sign the lease."

"But you GOT your $100!" said Mr. Markoff.

"But I haven't got the cottage," said Joe, sternly.

"Why," said Mr. Markoff, and the real Mrs. Markoff stood by him, "that sneaky so-and-so! I didn't like the look of him the minute he came in. Did you, dear?"

Mrs. Markoff agreed vehemently.

"I FELT there was something sneaky about him," said Markoff. "So I raised the rent $150 for the two

29

months, and made him pay it ALL in advance."

"Then," said Joe, "I suppose you have no objection to redeeming this receipt?"

"But you GOT your $100 back," puzzled Mr. Markoff.

"Not the $100 I gave you," said Joe.

Mr. Markoff pulled a wad from his pocket and, still looking puzzled, handed Joe ten $10 bills.

As we drove back out to the highway, Joe explained the morality of it.

"I'll use this extra hundred," he said, "to paint up Wesley's cottage, and make any repairs I see needed around. I hate to take it for free."

Things work out in the end.

Devotees

I could hardly believe it was Cooper's voice on the phone. "I can't go!" he said, hollowly.

"You can't WHAT?" I cried.

"Can't GO!" repeated Cooper.

"But we're leaving," I protested, "in less than an hour!"

Now, I don't know if you have any trout fishermen in your family or among your more intimate acquaintances. If you have not, you will hardly appreciate what the opening of the trout season means to the devotees of the Gentle Art.

Christmas is all very well. New Year, Easter, birthdays, wedding anniversaries—these are occasions that the trout fisherman can take or leave. But the opening day of the trout season is, you might say, the true New Year's Day to thousands upon thousands of otherwise normal men.

"Cooper," I asked brokenly, "you're kidding! What has happened?"

"Old Simily," he said, "can't find the Beattie and Bung contract."

"Beattie and Bung!" I snorted.

Old Simily—P. J. Simily—is general manager of the big contracting company of which Cooper is office manager.

"He says," went on Cooper pitiably, "he gave the contract to me. I swear he didn't. I swear I never saw it. And now there's some trouble over it, and 20 minutes ago, Old Simily, in an awful fit, told me not to leave the office until I find it and bring it up to him at his house. Tonight!"

I glanced at my watch. It was 5:15.

At 6, we were all to meet at W. C. Milne's office, change into our fishing clothes, and Milne would drive the three hours to our dear old familiar fishing resort where we four had opened the season for 16 years past.

"Cooper, listen!" I said. "I'll pick up Herriot, and he and I will go to Milne's office; and then the three of us will call and pick you up. That'll give you nearly an hour to find the thing. Get some of the girls to stay and help."

"They've all left," said Cooper, it being Friday afternoon. "No, you three go on without me."

"Never!" I said.

It would be unthinkable. Trout fishermen are bound by ties more mysterious and indestructible than those of mere friendship.

"We'll be there," I said firmly, "a little before 6:30."

I called Milne and Herriot and broke the news. Then I went around and collected Herriot, and we drove to Milne's office with our bags, and changed into our old clothes, the office being deserted of all save Milne.

Milne drove us to Cooper's, which is a small office building in front of the yards and warehouses of the construction company.

The caretaker didn't want to let us in. We sent him for Cooper, who came down and opened the door.

"I thought they was a bunch of bums," said the caretaker.

"Any sign of it?" I asked.

"Aw, listen," pleaded Cooper. "You fellows go on without me. There's 30 filing cabinets, hundreds of files. I may be all night!"

But we just headed up the stairs down which Cooper had come.

The big office was walled with steel filing cabinets.

"All right," said Cooper, wearily. "The file we are looking for is in an ordinary filing folder. It will be labelled Beattie and Bung on a blue label like this."

He showed us a file. Then with his keys he opened up three of the cabinets.

"You don't have to take them out," he explained. "Just rifle through them, looking at the labels."

We took off our old fishing coats and set to.

The caretaker watched us through the door.

By 7 p.m., we had each done only three of the six drawers of the first cabinets. We agreed to be slow and sure. By 7:45, we had finished the first cabinets.

"Aw," begged Cooper, "look, boys. Go on! It will be nearly midnight when you get up there."

But we just signalled him to unlock three more cabinets.

At 8, somebody came up the stairs. It was old P. J. Simily.

"Who," he barked from the door, "are these people, Cooper?"

Cooper explained we were his fishing companions with whom he had been intending to go fishing to celebrate the opening of the trout season, and we were just lending him a hand searching for the Beattie and Bung contract.

"Good heavens!" said Old Simily, stamping into the room. "Strangers snooping in our files, Cooper? Thanks to the caretaker, he telephoned me that there were some pretty shabby characters up here with you."

Cooper introduced us. I had met Mr. Simily three or four times before, but it had never taken, so to speak. I was identified as a newspaperman, Milne as a lawyer, in the roofing business, Herriot as an advertising man.

"I'd prefer," said Old Simily suspiciously, "if you carried the files over to the desk there for Cooper, and let HIM go through them."

We obeyed. Old Simily came and sat on a chair to watch.

"I never had much use," he said, "for grown men who carry childish sports and hobbies into maturity."

"Well, sir," I said, carrying more files, "it isn't exactly a sport or a hobby. It is a kind of infatuation."

"Bosh!" said Mr. Simily. "By the time a man is your age, he should realize there is only one interest to which he is entitled, and that is business. How do you suppose I became general manager of this company? By filling my head with trivialities? By trying to conceal my lack of industry by joining golf clubs, going to hockey games, following the horses, all in the name of recreation?"

Mr. Simily is a rather skinny man. I don't think he could hit a golf ball any distance.

But he had an audience.

"No, my boys," he enunciated. "I am glad, in a way, that this Beattie and Bung thing has developed. It bears out, perfectly, my principles. Here you have been, Cooper, for the past month, dreaming at your desk. Every day closer to May you have had a foolish look on you. Don't think I haven't noticed it! Goodness knows where you may have stuck that Beattie and Bung contract. And on Monday, if it can't be found, and the directors hear of it, I assure you, Cooper . . . "

Mr. Simily halted. He half rose from the chair. Then he bleated. That is exactly what he did. He bleated.

He ran from the room to his office.

After some delay, he returned.

"Here it is, Cooper," he said, modestly. "I just remembered that I had filed it with some insurance papers in my desk."

We all stood up and looked at him.

"I can't IMAGINE," he said, "how it could have slipped my mind."

We just stood. It was 8:45.

"Cooper, old man," he said, "don't bother coming in Monday. Stay an extra day on the fishing, eh? The directors are meeting Monday and . . . uh. You won't mention this to anyone, will you?"

On the way up to the fishing camp, we debated how long it will be before Cooper inherits Old Simily's job.

For man does not live by business alone.

The Tournament

Pinkerton, who has the fourth cottage west of us, came along the beach with his little nephew Ernie.

They both had fishing rods.

Harris, my next-door neighbor, was sitting on my steps with me.

"Not a bad day for it," said Harris. "Nice little ripple."

"That guy Pinkerton," I said, "can catch fish where there aren't any."

"I suppose he's teaching the kid the gentle art," reflected Harris.

"Hi!" called Pinkerton, turning up the path.

Ernie is a boy of seven, the dangerous age. He was carrying an old bait rod in one hand and a tomato can in the other. He had a purposeful look.

"Greg," said Pinkerton, "how would you like to lend Ernie and me your boat for a couple of hours? I can't get my engine to start."

"Aha," I said. "The usual trouble at the start of the season. Nothing works for the first few days. Sure you can have the boat. Are you going to introduce the young man to the gentle art?"

Pinkerton held up his rod. It was a beautiful delicate little spinning rod, with the odd-looking reel projecting out from its long cork handle.

"Going to do a little casting myself," smiled Pinkerton, "while Ernie dunks the old worm."

"I wanna catch FISH," announced Ernie, one of those hoarse little boys.

"Why," inquired Harris, "don't you teach the kid how to use the spinning rod, Pinkie? Any child can learn to fish with THAT outfit."

"I'm going to fish with WORMS," declared Ernie.

"Now, you take BAIT casting," said Harris. "There's an ART."

Pinkerton whipped the fragile little rod in his hand, a mere wisp.

"Bait casting!" he said. "That old stuff! That isn't fishing. That is bulldozing fish. Flinging great big plugs, on 20-pound lines, with those stubby little rods. Why, when you hook a fish, you just YANK him in! Now, with this spinning outfit, I use a four-pound monofilament line. This reel has a graduated brake on it, so that if more than a four-pound strain is put on the line, the reel SLIPS, and a fish has got a fighting chance."

"Can we go FISHING?" said little Ernie, hoarsely, but loud.

"Gentlemen," I said. "As a devotee of the fly rod, I would like to remark that one of the oldest and noblest styles of fishing is with a four-ounce rod, eight feet long, with a gossamer leader, and a tiny fly . . . "

"Hey!" said Pinkerton. "How about it? Why don't you two characters get your tackle, and we'll ALL take a whirl?"

Harris and I were already on our feet.

Little Ernie kicked the sand violently with one of his sneakers and headed down the path.

In five minutes, I was on my wharf with my third-best fly rod, a glass rod that I use as a knockabout. I had a streamer, a wet fly, on the leader.

Harris came bustling down with his bait-casting rod, a five-foot whip mounted with a multiplying, level-winding reel. On its end wobbled a large plastic plug, orange, with purple dots.

Ernie was hunched up in the bow of my boat,

sulking as only seven-year-olds can sulk.

Pinkerton was exuberant.

"We'll run over the Lord's Point," he said, "We'll fish and fish about. As challenger, I'll go first. Then, you, Harris come around with that monstrosity. Fish and fish about. Greg, we'll let you come third, with that fairy wand of yours."

"Aaarrrnnnfff!" said little Ernie, up in the bow.

"Now, now, Ernie," called Pinkerton. "You can fish while we're taking our turns."

"I wanna FISH!" cried Ernie.

I let Pinkerton run the engine. It started at the first pull, much to Pinkerton's surprise. We ran across to Lord's Point. We coasted in to a nice casting distance and turned off the engine.

Pinkerton stood up. He whipped the little spinning rod and the tiny lure, no bigger than a bride's engagement ring and just about as pretty, sailed through the air.

"Who's going to put on my WORM?" wailed Ernie.

Pfffft!

Pinkerton's lure jerked to a stop in mid air and fell to the water 30 feet away.

"Darn!" said Pinkerton.

His dainty little black reel was shrouded with a vast tangle of fragile nylon monofilament.

"O.K., Harris," he said sitting down. "Fire away while I . . ."

"Put on my WOORRRRMMM!" bellowed Ernie.

"Sssshhh!" said Pinkerton. "We're too far OUT for bait. Wait till we get in closer."

Harris stood up grandly. He made two or three practice swings with his stubby rod. Then he heaved-ho. The large plug arched through the air. Clunk! In mid air, it jerked back and fell with an obscene splash about 12 feet away. His reel seemed to be swollen with a mass of black line.

"O.K., Clark!" said Harris, sitting down.

Ernie, I observed, as I rose with my fly rod, was HIMSELF impaling a worm on his hook.

"Aaacchh!" he said.

I waved the fly rod. I let out line. I got 40 feet in the air, forward and back, forward and back.

"Clink!" went something.

I let the line fall on the water, and drew my rod, hand over hand, back into the boat.

"Hmmm!" I said. "The tip guide has come loose."

You can't fly-fish with no tip guide on the rod.

"Well, well, WELL!" I said to my companions, hunched over their tackle. "At the start of the season EVERYTHING seems to go wrong."

Up at the bow there was a tremendous splash.

For an instant, I thought little Ernie must have fallen overboard.

But then I saw he was half risen, his old bait rod arched magnificently.

"Hold him, boy!" I shouted. "HOLD him!"

"Let him RUN!" yelled Harris.

"Here," cried Pinkerton, "let me handle the . . . "

"Get away!" roared Ernie.

It was a four-pounder.

Man, what a beauty!

"A fish that size," said Pinkerton, "has no RIGHT coming right out ALONGSIDE a boat like that."

So we called it a day and steamed for home, Ernie to show his fish to all the kids along the Point, and the rest of us to untangle our back-lashes and re-cement our tip guides and that sort of thing.

O, Canadaw!

"O, Canadaw," sang Jimmie "de dum, de dum, de dum. Dum, dum, de dum . . ."

"Brrrrrr!" said I.

"As a matter of fact," said Jim, "there are a lot of people living in Canada and calling themselves Canadians who ought to get the heck out of here."

"Indeed," said I.

"Yes," went on Jim, "they ought to go on back home to England, Scotland or Ireland or wherever their misguided parents came from. Or else they ought to migrate to California or some other sissy clime."

"Is that so?" I argued.

"If a person finds," said Jim, "that he can't stand the climate, if he comes to the conclusion that a mistake has been made, even after two or three generations, he ought to quit beefing about the country and go on back home."

"Home," I snorted.

"Yes, home, wherever that is," declared Jim. "Because to tell you the truth, there is not, in the whole vast round world, a more beautiful, entrancing, satisfying country than Canada. Where else can you show me a land where, without moving a muscle, you can enjoy the luscious beauty of the tropics in summer and the glorious splendor of the Arctic in winter? Less fortunate people than Canadians, and by Canadians I mean those who can take it, have to go to Switzerland in the winter for a little skiing, and then move a thousand miles to the south of France or Surrey or County Antrim for a little beauty in the summer."

"A Canadian," I admitted, "has to have a versatile hide."

"Instead of agitating for more population," stated Jim, "I recommend that we comb out of the country all the belly-achers who bawl all summer about the heat and who squeal all winter about the cold."

"I wasn't squealing," I informed him. "I was merely saying that I would be glad to see the first of May, and the opening of the trout season."

"It often puzzles me," mused Jimmie, "that a man as fond of fishing as you are doesn't go ice-fishing."

"Ice-fishing," I replied, "is for them as likes it. First of all, there is the long drive over wintry roads up to some place around the North Pole. Then there is the locating of some queer old duck who owns a few fishing huts. Usually, you spend about three hours trailing him around a village of seventeen houses, and when you do find him, he has rented all his huts for the day."

"Then," said Jim, "there is the long walk, with icy wind digging in under your chin and forcing you to shut your eyes, while you cross glare ice two miles to the right spot where the fishing huts have been placed."

"The huts," I said, "are about four feet square. Inside is a bench, a stove made out of a gasoline can, and a hole in the ice about the size of a suit-case."

"Correct," said Jim. "And you inhale wood smoke from the gimcrack little stove; and if you check it down, you freeze; and if you let it burn up, you smother."

"Yes," I agreed, "and you sit, bent over in that tiny little shack, with nobody to talk to. And you dangle a line from your hand, baited with a minnow, down into the green depth. That shadowy, mysterious green depth; and hour by hour, as you sit there bent over, sniffling, coughing and peering, suddenly, suddenly your heart stands still . . . "

"A shadow," said Jim. "A ghostly shadow stirs in that jade-green depth. Suddenly, like a streak of silver, a herring, soundless, swift, dreamlike, darts like a flicker of light, across the dimness!"

"Then," I cried, "two, three, twenty, fifty, a thousand! The herring streaming, silent, soundless, glorious, beautiful, across your vision. Jimmie, let's go! When can we leave?"

"We could leave now," said Jim, distastefully eyeing his drawing board.

So we went, and through a dry blizzard that tinkled small countless flakes of snow against our windshield, we drove north fifty miles to the lake and drew rein at one of those little villages which in summer are so busy, and in winter, so silent, sleeping.

At the gas station, we asked who owned fishing huts for rent and were given the name of a gentleman who spent part of his time snaring rabbits, part of it cutting wood, and the rest of it renting fishing huts. And as was expected, we spent all of an hour tracking him down in that hamlet of eleven silent white houses. We located him at last at the gas station, where he had been all the time sitting in the back, but nobody had noticed him.

"Gentlemen," he said, "I've rented four of my five shacks this morning. But I have one left for this afternoon, and I was figuring on doing a little fishing myself. But I'll let you have it, rather than see youse disappointed after your long drive."

"Have they been catching any fish this last

while?"

"It was real good about two weeks ago," said he. "But they are getting plenty right now. I wouldn't be surprised when we get out there to find they've had a record catch. This here hole I will take you to, there was 400 herring taken out of it three days ago."

Jim and I exchanged a look. It was a matter of moments for Jim and me to change out of our city clothes into our mackinaw coats and leather topped rubbers. And all arcticked up, we joined the old man for the tramp across the icy waste to the fishing huts visible far out on the lake. There were about fifteen houses clustered together. Like dots they were in the afternoon blizzard. The wind raked across the ice and gathered a sort of concentrated chill. In us, the wind found something to cuddle to, for warmth. It fairly embraced us.

"Chah," we breathed through bare teeth, bowing our heads and following the rapid footsteps of our guide.

The wind was stronger than ever, and by the time we got half way out to the fishing huts, I was for turning around and heading for any of the various parts of Scotland from which my misguided forebears came. I would even eat haggis. I would even sit, in a kilt, on the top of Ben Lomond.

But though I felt my brain congealing and trying to push, like the cream on a milk bottle, out the top of my head; and though my ears went numb and my cheekbones ached with cold, we finally reached the fishing huts; and at our approach, a hairy-chested man in his undershirt stepped out of one of the tin shacks to welcome us.

"How's she doing?" asked the old man guiding us.

"I got six herring and a whitefish," said the stranger.

"Anybody else doing anything?"

"Everybody's got a few," said he. "There's going to be a blow. You can tell. The fish are heading out deep."

"Well, anyway," said our guide, leading us down past a double row, a sort of street of fish huts, to one at the far end.

He lighted the gasoline can stove with kindling, I struggled inside the tiny cubicle to warm my frigid members, and the old chap, with a big chisel fastened to a rake handle, jabbed away the fresh ice out of the fishing hole in the floor of the hut. He scooped out the cracked ice and checked off the stove.

"If she don't show you any fish in half an hour," said he, "I'll stick around and move you to a fresh hole. I know a hole over here a ways where two weeks ago, a party of us got 400 herring."

Removing our heavy coats, Jim and I sat in the little hut, side by side, and prepared our lines. The lines were wound on a stick bobbin, and on the hook we impaled an inch-long minnow of which our guide left a lard-pail full.

So far back in our language that the schools think nobody but scholars are interested, there are tales of dragons and monsters inhabiting the depths of the sea; Beowulf is one, and the chill and slimy clasp of Grendl is another; and since we all come from little islands hemmed about by the sea, and since rooted in our very souls are the tales of the sea, and the dark humor of the sea, and the darker fear of it, there is a curious homesickness that touches us as we sit in the fishing hut watching down into the depths. For the first few moments of mesmeric staring in the window through the ice of a fishing hut, we are of this time and of this place; but presently, the faint forgotten legends of our blood begin to stir. That dim green window in the ice beckons. Down in its eerie kingdom, dreams abide. Within an hour of watching in that jadey half-light, a man goes fey. He is half tempted to lean a little too far forward, to pitch down and dive forever into the adventures of the past and of the future.

"Jiggle your bait," said Jim, thickly, after the first hour.

"I haven't seen so much as a mudcat," I husked.

And for another half hour, we sat, jiggling and staring.

"Some wind," said Jim.

"It's a gale," I admitted. "I hope it will be behind us and not against us."

A rap on our door roused us from our dozing.

"They're biting over a bit," shouted the old man. "I'll go cut a hole for you. Get the shack on the runners."

We donned our mackinaws and went out into the hurricane. Dusty snow was whirling and dirling. The houses next door were half obscured by the rushing mist of snow. The sleigh-like runners on which the fishing huts are moved about from place to place were leaning against our shack. With a shovel, we broke away the snow packed around the bottom of the hut. With a skilful tilt, Jim hoisted one end of the shack on to the runners.

"Where to now?" I cried, looking about for our guide. But in the blizzard he was nowhere to be seen. Out of all the other little shacks, merry smoke curled and eddied.

We shoved the little shack down the aisle of

houses, the wind helping us. We turned it, and shoved it back. No sign of our old friend.

"Where's he gone?" asked Jim, peering into the blast.

"Well, I'm not going to freeze," I said, "let him come and get us when he's ready."

And I got inside the shack and fed a few more sticks into the fire. And in a jiffy, Jim joined me.

"Some climate," said I.

"We'll get fish in the next hole," said Jim, unbuttoning his mackinaw. "You never get fish in the first hole, ice fishing."

"Jim," said I, "we're moving."

"So we are," said Jim. "Maybe the old gent is pushing us to the new hole."

We felt the house gliding smoothly across the ice, with tiny ribby sounds.

"Let him push," said I.

We waited.

"Seems like quite a long push," said Jim, reaching up to unlatch the door.

And then I knew, by the smooth, racing, pebbly, humming sound of our runners on the ice that no human hand was pushing us.

"Kick her open," I shouted.

"The button outside must have dropped," cried Jim, thumping against the door. In the eerie flicker of the small fire, I could see he was putting his weight into it.

"Jim," I bellowed.

For now I knew the wind had us, and the sound of the runners on the ice rose to a high and throbbing hum. The tiny shack seemed to lift like an iceboat on the fury of the gale, and loved it.

"Jim," I cried, "get a pick. Get anything. Kick a board out."

"That's what I'm doing," grunted Jim.

But the men who build fishing huts are lazy, patient men. When they nail on a board, they nail it on. We kicked. We joined forces and shoved. We rocked it. But we could not rock it over.

"Take it easy," shouted Jim above the throbbing sound of the ice racing underneath our runners. "The whole lake is frozen over. Sooner or later we land up with a bump on shore."

"Very well," I agreed, "let us sit back and enjoy it. Do you suppose such a thing as this ever happened to anybody before."

And Jim gallantly leaned forward and fed some more kindling into the stove.

We bumped over ridges, we careened over drifts. We slowed up and then gained speed. The wind had us, and the wind did with us what it liked.

"How far can we go?" I asked.

"If we hit the narrows," said Jim, "we can go up into the next lake. And if we were to strike the river, we might go thirty miles. But . . . "

"Jim," I said, "I think I heard voices."

We listened. Undoubtedly, there was a shout.

"Hey," yelled a voice, and something struck our walls.

Zip, went the runners. Zip, zip, and then a terrific splash.

"Good-bye, Jim," I roared.

For icy green water was gushing up from the hole in the floor through which we were lately fishing; and the big home-made sled on which the house had stood, started slipping away from under us.

Then outside, voices shouted unintelligibly. In chorus, Jim and I replied. We felt the fish house heave and fall, and we were flung on our backs as it rolled over. We heard a hand scrabbling with the button that locked us in.

And then glorious daylight burst upon us.

Jim was first out. The scene that met my gaze was enough to freeze an Eskimo's marrow. Seven men with a team of horses were grouped about in attitudes of astonishment. They were cutting ice, and wide lanes of green water gaped before us. In one of them, our sled bobbed peacefully. And our shack lay on its back on the edge of the perilous gulf.

"Gentlemen," I said to the group of rescuers. "On behalf of both of us, I wish to express our thanks."

They grinned at us eagerly, and the two nearest us shook their heads.

"No spik," said the first man, and the others added, "no spik."

"Don't speak English?" I asked.

"No spik," they all agreed heartily. Such big, ruddy men they were. With wide faces and bare throats and chests, and glowing cheeks and an air of might about them. The blizzard seemed to be agreeable to them, the way they stood up to it, eyes open.

"No spik?" I asked. "What are you? Italiano?"

"Suomi," said the first one, and all the others nodded their heads and added "Suomi."

"Finns, Jim," I translated. "And I guess that dim shadow over there is land. What do you say if we head for land?"

"Land, ho," agreed Jim.

So we shook hands, mitts and all, with our seven friends, and walked for the shore while they stood and gazed with amazement.

"Jim," I said, as we neared what was undoubtedly

terra firma, "what do you say if we hand this country over to the Finns?"

"Let's stick around until May," said Jim, "before we decide."

The Joker

Here she comes!" announced Joe Baker heartily.

"Thank heavens," I said to myself.

At the end of a week's fishing trip, you can get awfully tired of even your oldest and best friends.

In another five minutes, I would be at peace in the privacy of my roomette.

The four of us, with our four guides, began grabbing up our baggage, our bundles of fishing rods, packsacks, duffle bags and portable ice boxes full of trout. Out in the night and the rain, the trans-continental with its blazing headlight was thundering to a slow stop at this little station away up in the spruce and the muskeg. It was 10:43 p.m.

The guides carrying the heavy stuff, we headed out on to the rainy platform while the engineer of the massive train manoeuvred it to bring the sleeping cars as near as possible for the sportsmen he knew he had to pick up at this flag stop.

We hurried down the cinder-and-mud path.

"Here's ours," sang out Cooper.

And he and Herriot were helped aboard by the porter and the guides.

Joe Baker and I had to slosh four more sleeping cars, almost to the end of the train, before we found Car 2218. We hardly had time to fling our stuff into the vestibule and shake hands with our guides before the train creaked into motion.

"That Cooper," said Joe Baker, "is a lucky stiff. Imagine! He gets the first car!"

The porter left our ice boxes and most of our heavy duffle stacked out in the vestibule.

"They'll be safe there," he assured us, as he showed us to our roomettes.

I had got my jacket off and sunk on to the comfortable seat when Joe Baker came in and sat on the only other accommodation in the little roomette.

"That lucky stiff, Cooper!" he said, lighting a cigarette. "He not only gets the best trout, and the MOST trout, but he picks the sleeper that stops practically at the platform! On a night like this!"

"Aw, waw." I yawned in agreement, as a hint.

"Listen," said Joe. "I'm going to have some fun with Cooper. In a little while, when everything's quiet, I'm going ahead to see if HIS ice box is in their vestibule. And if it IS, I'm going to switch his trout into MY box."

"Aw now, Joe," I protested. "No more TRICKS!"

Joe is one of those indefatigable jokers. All week, he had been subjecting the rest of us to his humorous gags. When we went out in the morning, we couldn't find our rods. Naturally, on a fishing trip, nobody is QUITE sure where he left his fly rod the night before, on coming in. If we played cards, all the aces would have been removed from the pack. When we picked up the salt cellar in the grumpy morning to sprinkle our breakfast trout, the top would fall off. He was THAT sort of joker.

"We'll just finish off the trip," gloated Joe, "with one GOOD one! One dandy!"

I was tucked in bed when my roomette buzzer buzzed. It was Joe.

"Done!" he whispered gleefully through my curtains. "Got them all. Wait till he gets HOME and opens the box . . . "

When we arrived in the city at 8 a.m., Joe, who is a masterly type, got a redcap right away. We loaded our gear on his truck and hustled down the platform in time to catch Cooper and Herriot, who hadn't even got a redcap yet. We piled all our stuff on the one truck and headed for the taxi tank.

Joe Baker was jubilant, as only jokers can be that early in the morning.

"It's been a wonderful trip!" he boomed at us. "Cheer up, you guys!"

Cooper and Herriot shared one taxi, as they live close to each other. Joe and I shared the next one, since we live only six blocks apart.

"What do you plan to do now?" I inquired, as we drove into town.

"Around 10," said Joe, "I'll pick you up, and we'll call at Cooper's apartment WITH the fish!"

"I . . . uh . . . " I attempted evasive action. The fishing trip was OVER, as far as I was concerned.

"Aw, come AWN!" said Joe. "I like witnesses to my little gags."

At 10, he phoned. At 10:10, he picked me up. At 10:20, we drew in beside Cooper's apartment house. Joe carried his ice box discreetly as we entered the foyer. Took the elevator up to the fourth floor. Went along to Cooper's apartment.

Joe set the ice box down a few feet from the door, out of sight.

Cooper, in his dressing gown, opened to us. "Hel-LO!" he cried cheerily, surprised.

"Just passing," said Joe Baker. "How's everything?"

"Fine," said Cooper.

"Fish get home in good shape?" asked Joe.

"Perfect," said Cooper. "We shared one of the small ones for breakfast. Delicious."

"Eh?" said Joe.

"Come on in," said Cooper, "and have a cup of coffee with us."

Mrs. Cooper appeared from the kitchen.

"They're BEAUTIFUL," she said. "We put the rest of them in the freezer, and I'm going to have a BIG family party."

"You GOT them?" interrupted Joe.

"How do you mean?" asked Cooper.

Joe Baker stared around at us with an expression of mounting horror.

"Folks," he said. "There's something wrong. Last night, for a little gag, I went ahead in the sleepers with my ice box and PINCHED your trout."

"Oh, THAT!" said Cooper. "There was another ice box, a tartan-colored one, just like mine, already in the vestibule. So I took MINE into my compartment with me."

"Oh, good grief!" said Joe, sagging.

"I asked the porter whose it was," went on Cooper, "and he said it belonged to an old Judge McDougall."

"McDougall!" cried Joe, leaping up. "You mean the one that's on the Police Commission?"

Joe sank back on to his chair, not unlike a poached egg.

"He'll have all the police force," gasped Joe, "the detectives, the railway police . . ."

"Listen," said Cooper. "Go and call his house! Quick! Explain there has been a mistake. Say you'll deliver the trout right away."

Joe rushed to the phone, scrambled through the telephone book, dialled the number. He engaged in an excited conversation we didn't quite overhear.

"That was his wife," said Joe. "She says the judge hasn't been fishing for 10 years."

"O.K., Joe," said Cooper, putting his arm around his wife's shoulder and facing him. "Go and get the ice box. It's in the hall, isn't it? We saw you arrive and carry it in."

"Whaaaaattt?" cried Joe.

"Before we got into the station this morning," said Cooper, "I had a look and found my box empty except for the ice. I figured it was you. So I bet my wife two bucks you would arrive before 10:30. Bring her in!"

Joe went and brought in the ice box. "That," he declared indignantly, "was a dirty trick!"

Reek

You never really know your luck. For instance, it being less than 30 days until the opening of the trout season in these parts, I was naturally pretty excited after I met Harry Garnett and his wife downtown Tuesday afternoon.

"By the way," said Harry, "I suppose you've heard about poor old Mr. Adamson?"

"No!" said I, shocked.

"Well, he had a little stroke last Christmas," said Harry, "and he's given up fishing."

"Holy doodle!" said I.

"Yes," said Harry, "and he's giving away all his stuff. He gave the two heart specialists each one of his best fly rods."

"The French ones?" I exclaimed unhappily.

"I guess so," said Harry. "And then I've heard of

half a dozen others who have called to see him. And they came away with boxes full of his choicest trout flies. Some got leather rod cases, reels, $15 fly lines."

"And books," put in Mrs. Garnett, "from his library. He's got the loveliest angling library in Canada."

"Holy doodle!" I reiterated, tingling all over.

"My wife and I," smiled Harry, "are going to run up to see him on the weekend. He's at his farm, with a nurse. He's quit all business."

"Well, well, well!" said I.

And then, for fear the Garnetts might see something in my face, I changed the subject, and as soon as convenient bade them adieu.

Dear old Mr. Adamson. What a pity. His fishing days ended.

But if he still had one of those French fly rods in his possession, it was my DUTY to go and see him. Just because a man is a heart specialist is no reason why he should have one of Mr. Adamson's French fly rods. A man has to be a post-graduate ordained, consecrated, Ph.D. of fly fishing to handle one of those. Mr. Adamson used to go over to Paris every couple of years and visit the custom-rod makers and try out 30 to 40 of these hand-made jewels and bring home two or three of the choicest.

Of course, people like me couldn't afford them. Only old financiers like Mr. Adamson could indulge in such superlative . . . But if he were GIVING them away!

By the strangest coincidence, it just so happened that I had to go to Brockville on Wednesday on business. And Mr. Adamson's farm is about halfway to Brockville, necessitating only a 10-mile side trip off the main highway.

What more natural than that I should drop in to see the dear old gentleman, perhaps taking him a small gift of some kind, one of those wicker-basket things prettily stuffed with fruit and small jars of jelly and things. And maybe the latest issues of the outdoor magazines, just to turn the conversation toward fishing.

With me, no sooner thought of than done.

I got to the turn-off up to the village near which Mr. Adamson's farm is located, just about 1:15. There was a good big wayside restaurant at the crossroads, so I decided to go in and have a leisurely lunch so as not to arrive while Mr. Adamson was having an afternoon nap, and the nurse might just accept the basket and send me on my way. About 3 p.m. would be a good time to arrive.

Shortly after 2 p.m. I went into the gents' washroom to wash up before setting on my way.

The washroom was one of these new-fangled affairs. Instead of a roller towel, or even paper towels, it had an electric hand dryer. You wash your hands, then touch a button on this box on the wall. And from a large faucet, a blast of hot air blows out. You rub your hands together under the hot air. Very sanitary.

And above the hand-dryer is another contraption. It is an enamelled box with four small nozzles projecting from it. And over each nozzle is a metal label; cologne, lavender, shave lotion and hair dressing. You put a dime in your choice. And a mist of masculine cosmetic sprays on you.

While I was washing my hands, three loud young duck-tail types swarmed into the washroom, shouting in their characteristic fashion to one another. And the first thing they did was stick a dime in the cologne and spray themselves. I moved to the hand-dryer. But such is the impertinence of these hot-rodders toward their elders that one of them leaned over me and stuck a dime in the hair-do nozzle, and sprayed his already slathery locks with some highly-scented mist.

I was glad to get out of the washroom, even though my hands were not quite dry.

When I arrived at Mr. Adamson's farm—which really isn't a farm as you and I know farms; it is a show place which Mr. Adamson has hired farmers to operate as a pure-bred country estate for the past 20 years—a middle-aged nurse opened the door. I held my gift basket well back, so she couldn't take it.

"I was just passing," I said. "And it occurred to me Mr. Adamson might care to see another old fly fisher."

"Why, of course!" cried the nurse cheerily. "He's just up from his nap. He always likes to see his fishing friends."

She led me into the library where Mr. Adamson was seated in an easy chair busy wrapping fresh tape around a landing-net handle.

"Remember me, Mr. Adamson?" I cried heartily. "I ran into you on the Nipigon back in 1919, remember?"

Mr. Adamson was regarding me enthusiastically.

"Why, sure!" he said. "Smith, isn't it? Or Jones?"

"No, Clark," I explained.

"Of course," cried Mr. Adamson reaching out his hand. "One of those short names."

I stepped over and pumped his hand heartily.

"Aha!" I said, bending over to inspect his handiwork. "I see you are getting ready for the season!"

Mr. Adamson thrust me away.

"Sit over there, will you?" he directed, pointing to

another easy chair across the room.

He fanned the air with landing net.

"No, young man," he said. "I guess you haven't heard that I am finished as far as fishing is concerned."

"Mr. Adamson!" I protested. "Don't tell me that!"

"Yep," he said. "Through. Finished. Whew!"

"Well, I heard you had been laid up," I said. "And since I was passing by, I thought I should drop in and say hello. But I had no idea . . ."

The nurse brought in the basket.

"See what Mr. Smith has brought you," she beamed.

"Clark," said I, amiably.

"Phew!" said Mr. Adamson.

He asked me what business I was in. He checked on where I had met him on the Nipigon. We explored around and found several mutual acquaintances among our fishing friends. But Mr. Adamson seemed ill at ease. After we had recounted the various places we had mutually fished—Newfoundland, the Yukon, Queen Charlotte Islands, Quebec—Mr. Adamson asked me to go and call Mrs. Finch, his nurse.

When she came, Mr. Adamson said he had to go and lie down again for a while.

Trusting that I had not disturbed him with my visit, I made as polite an exit as I could, Mrs. Finch helping me on with my coat and more or less bustling me out the vestibule.

I didn't go on to Brockville after all. I drove home.

Last night, Harry Garnett telephoned me around 9.

"Hi!" he cried. "I hear you were in to see Mr.

Adamson the other day."

"Just in passing," I admitted.

"He's a funny old boy," laughed Garnett. "You must have rubbed him the wrong way. He said he can't STAND a man who uses perfume."

"Perfume!" I scoffed.

"He said you were all stunk up with perfume," said Garnett. "You reeked."

Then Garnett said he and his wife were just back from spending the afternoon and having supper with the old man.

"We each," said he, "got a French rod!"

"Wonderful!" I cried.

As I say, you never really know your luck.

The silliest things can happen, even in wash-rooms, in wayside eating joints.

Things that can alter your entire fortune.

The Fish

H ow would you like a couple of nice fish?" It was young Henderson on the phone. He lives in the upper duplex across the street.

"Wonderful!" I exclaimed.

"My crazy brother," said Henderson, "up in the north country, has sent us a 40-pound box of fish! It just came by express."

"Forty pounds!" I gloated. "What kind are they?"

"Whitefish, I expect," said Henderson, "and lake trout. I haven't opened them yet."

"Man!" I breathed.

"Well, yes," said Henderson, "but WE haven't got

room in our freezer for 40 pounds! Holy smoke! That's this brother of mine all over."

Henderson has frequently mentioned his older brother, an engineer for one of the big oil companies travelling all over the far north on exploration work; a bachelor; a kind of adventurer, it seems. I would like to know him.

"What we're doing," said Henderson, "is calling up a couple of the chaps from my office, and you, and one or two of the neighbors."

"Well, it's most kind," I said. "There is nothing I like better than a feed of good fresh fish from the north. Probably caught through the ice."

"Have you got any old newspapers you can spare?" asked Henderson. "If you'd bring them over, to wrap the fish when the people come . . . "

"Delighted," I said, for newspapermen always have a pile of old newspapers in the pantry. "When would you like me to come over?"

"Any time now," said Henderson. "The others are likely to be along shortly."

When I climbed the stairs to Henderson's home with my armload of newspapers, Mrs. Parker, one of the neighbors, and Jones, who lives next door to them, were already on hand.

"Isn't this lovely?" cried Mrs. Parker. "Fresh fish, right down from the Arctic!"

"This big brother of ours!" said young Mrs. Henderson. "He's always doing the craziest things. Even if we HAD room in our freezer, we'd be sick of fish by the time we'd eaten half of them. Forty pounds!"

"Maybe," I suggested, "he knew you would have the pleasure of giving your neighbors a treat. Where's the box? I'll help."

"I left it in the basement," explained Henderson. "We'll go down and divvy them up when the others get here."

Two lively young men from Henderson's office arrived, and after we had been introduced around, we all descended to the basement of the duplex, with the old newspapers.

On the cement floor was the box, roped and most sturdily packed. It was not even leaking.

"Where was it shipped from?" I inquired, studying the labels.

"I can't make out," said Henderson, cutting the cords. "It may have come from Yellowknife, or Churchill, on Hudson Bay, or even Whitehorse. He's all over the place. Travels by air, of course."

When we got the outer heavy paper wrapping off, there was an inner burlap covering, sewed.

"It's good and cold," I remarked. "Well packed."

"They'll be in prime condition," agreed Jones.

The inner container was a double-thick carton. Henderson pried loose the staples and spread the lids back.

On top of the frosty packages was an envelope containing a note. Henderson took it over under the cellar light. He started to read:

"Dear Smog-Bound Brother:

"The company is sending me off to Mexico for three months, so I have to clean out my freezer locker here. I trust you will have some fun with these contents. I got the ptarmigan in . . ."

Henderson lowered the note and stared a little pallidly around the circle of us. We had all our eyebrows raised.

Slowly he lifted the note, and after a moment, in a less enthusiastic voice, continued:

"I got the ptarmigan over on the west shore of James Bay. The ruffed grouse, or partridge, as you no doubt call them, in Labrador. The mallards . . . ”

Henderson paused, and cast a piteous glance at his wife. She lowered her gaze.

“The mallards,” read Henderson, in a weak voice. “I got in Saskatchewan. The small roast is caribou, from the Eskimos, a choice loin roast. The large package is a couple of moose steaks from the Kenai Peninsula. I am labelling the box ‘Fish’ so the express company will handle it faster, and the handlers be less curious as to its contents. With love to my poor little civilized sister and brother,

“AL”

Henderson tossed the note on the box, covered his mouth with his hand, and hung his head.

Young Mrs. Henderson was the first to speak.

“Actually,” she said, rather thinly, “I’ve got quite a BIT of room in our freezer. That is, I wouldn’t make room for FISH, but . . . ”

“Ptarmigan!” said Jones. “I’ve never TASTED ptarmigan!”

“Caribou,” I remarked, “is DELICIOUS.”

One of the young fellows from Henderson’s office bent down to the box.

“Let’s,” he said, “have a LOOK at it, anyway.”

Coming out of his trance, Henderson officiated. The packages, neatly done up in heavy brown waxed paper, were labelled in heavy crayon.

“Four ptarmigan!” intoned Henderson.

Next:

“Four ruffed grouse!”

Next:

“Four mallard!”

Mrs. Henderson had loosened the corner of one package, and peeked.

“They’re all drawn and cleaned!” she murmured.

61

There was a roast of caribou and a massive package labelled "Sirloin of Moose."

On the bottom was a last package, larger than the rest.

"Five lake trout," It was marked.

"FISH!" shouted Henderson, his voice cracking with joy.

So the two young chaps from the office, Mrs. Parker, Jones and I each got, as promised, a lovely 2½-pound choice lake trout, straight from the far north.

Bick's Crick

Oho! Bick's Crick. Here we had it at last!

Herriot was driving. I was sitting beside him with the map spread out on my knees. Frank Cooper was in the back seat, leaning forward to help me read the map.

"Whoa!" I cried triumphantly.

And Herriot pulled the car to a stop on the gravel road, just where a side road led to the right.

"Look there," I commanded, my finger tip on the map.

Herriot and Cooper bent close. On the map was printed the little thread of blue indicating a stream or river. I traced the blue thread with my finger two inches to a small square dot. And in tiny type by the dot were the words: Bick's Mill.

"We've got it!" we all cried simultaneously.

For us three, this was the joyous conclusion to three years of sly and subtle search. Bick's Crick had become to us a sort of Holy Grail. We had heard of it only five or six times. But each time, it was from a trout fisherman of the highest standing. We had seen snapshots of the trout taken from Bick's Crick. We had even eaten a couple of gift trout taken from Bick's Crick.

They were none of your slim, pallid trout such as you get in ponds and wide gravelly streams. No. These were short, stout, dark trout, almost a milk-chocolate color on the back, and the contrasting fins of white and orange so vivid as to look painted on. The scarlet spots, ringed with iridescent blue, were like jewels set amid the rich olive brown of the trout's flanks.

These were the fabulous trout of Bick's Crick, a small, full, quiet-running creek hidden in this valley amid the farms. A hundred springs of pure, ice-cold water were said to feed it as it wandered amid deep silent swamps of cedar. Nowhere in its length of seven or eight miles, before it ran forth into the open farm country, could you cast a fly in it as you would on a pond. You had to crawl, so our bits and pieces of information told us, amid the cedars and alders, finding the quiet holes, three feet deep and no bigger than a bath tub. You dibbled your fly on a short line on the stealthy waters of these holes.

And from the shadowed depths would coil these dark and lustrous trout, 12, 15, even 18 inches long, a pound to two pounds each.

"We turn here," I stated.

"No," said Cooper, "Look. Take the next turn, one concession on. There's only the one farm marked on it. And we can walk back from that farm, see, to the valley. That will be right in the thick of the bush."

"He's right," said Herriot.

So, with beating hearts, it being only 10 o'clock of a perfect trout morning, soft south wind, hazy overcast, we drove one concession farther, turned right on a very rough dirt road, and came, within half a mile, to the farmhouse that was indicated on the map.

The farmer was working on the engine of a tractor when we drove into his yard.

"Good morning, sir," we said, bailing out.

"Good morning," agreed the farmer, a big, sandy man with a friendly disposition.

"Does Bick's Crick," asked Herriot, "run at the back of your place, in that valley over there?"

"It does," said the farmer.

"We understand there's trout in it," said Cooper.

"Plenty of them," said the farmer. "Oodles."

"Well," I negotiated, "would it be all right if we walked back and did a little fishing?"

"It's O.K. with me," said the farmer heartily.

"Do you charge anything for a day's fishing?" asked Cooper.

"I'm a farmer," said he, "not a fish dealer."

He beamed at us.

So we arranged to leave our car in his yard. And after thanking him most warmly, we unpacked our rods and fly boxes, hauled on our hip rubber boots, and in 10 minutes were marching across the pasture, climbing the fences, hoofing it along the margins of wheat fields, to come at last to the end of the open fields. And there, below us in the wide valley, spread the dark expanse of the cedar swamp within whose mysterious stillness meandered Bick's Crick.

"I'll walk up two fields north here," said Herriot, "and then head in and fish down. You, Greg, head in here, and fish down toward me. Frank, you go

64

two fields south and head in and fish down toward Greg. That'll give us all a fair deal, and we'll meet at 1 p.m. right here, for sandwiches. O.K.?"

My partners hurried off in their directions. I dived into the cedars.

It was not a hundred yards through fairly open cedar groves before I came to Bick's Crick. It was all that we had dreamed. Its average width would be no more than eight feet, here and there narrowing to four feet to form deep, log-dammed pools fringed with luscious ferns. Its current was slow, with that full, silent sweep that bespoke the countless springs that fed its volume. I jointed up and threaded my rod and put on a size 10 Professor Cash, a good fly to start with anywhere, to see what they were taking.

Moving with utmost caution so as not to joggle the soft earth of the cedar swamp and so warn the trout of my approach, I reached the rod out and dropped the fly on the first pool, intending to dibble it seductively like a struggling insect, on the surface.

CLUNK!

My rod was chucked violently downward. I hoisted instinctively. And out on to the bank before me was hoisted a leaping, frenzied and gorgeous trout of 14 inches. I plunged and tackled him, football fashion: hugged him to my breast.

Ladies and gentlemen, though it was an awful way for a dedicated fly fisherman to dibble and hoist lovely trout out of these tangled hide-aways of Bick's Crick, I took four from the first hole, four from the second, and had two already out of the third hole I came to, when I saw Herriot bending and pushing through the cedars toward me.

"Holy smoke!" I greeted him. "Did you

ever . . . ?"

And then I saw he was not alone.

A stormy-faced man was walking immediately behind him. And back of that man was a third in the uniform of the county police.

"It seems," said Herriot, as I stood up, "we are on private property."

"But the farmer," I protested, "told us we . . ."

"HE don't own this property," said the stormy-faced man in a loud voice. "THIS property is leased to a private club by me. I'M the owner, see? My farm runs back up that hill to HIS."

"But," I cut in, "shouldn't you put signs up back here to show . . . ?"

"I DO!" shouted the stormy one. "But SOME-BODY pulls them down as fast as I put them UP!"

The constable stood back, poker-faced.

"I'll go and get Cooper," said Herriot.

I gathered my rod, bag and trout.

"I'LL take the trout, thanks," said the stormy one.

I then saw he had five others, taken from Herriot.

"I'll accompany you out to your car," said the constable.

We left the stormy one, heading back his way. The constable and I went up the hill and out to the farm where our car waited.

Our farmer was still working on the tractor engine.

"Well," he said.

"I thought you told us," I accused, "we could fish back there."

"No," said the big sandy fellow, amiably. "All I said was, it was O.K. with me."

As I stowed my gear in the car, awaiting Herriot

66

and Cooper, the constable got in the back, suggesting we drive him to his car at the other farm.

"You boys," he said, quietly, "just got mixed up in one of these back-country feuds. These two farmers' families haven't been speaking for three generations."

The Dip

Hey!" barked my old friend Dandy Daniels over the phone. "Didn't you mention you were going smelt-fishing?"

"As a matter of fact, Dandy," I said, "I'm going tonight. Leaving in less than an hour."

"I'm going with you," announced Dandy.

This was preposterous.

"Aw, now, Dandy!" I protested.

He is far past 80. It is true he is remarkably well-preserved for so old a man, full of spirit and gumption.

"Pick me up," he ordered, "in 30 minutes. I'll be ready."

"Now, wait a minute," I cried. "You couldn't POSSIBLY go smelt-fishing. It's all in the middle of the night. The run doesn't start until midnight or even 2 o'clock . . ."

"Thirty minutes," shouted Dandy. "I'll be all set."

And he clattered the phone down.

What in the world can you do with these old characters? I put my hip rubber boots and mackinaw coat in the car, and I felt my night of smelt-fishing was already ruined.

As I drove across town to Dandy's trim little home where he lives with Hortense, his housekeeper of 40 years long suffering, the prospect of having old Dandy on my hands for the night loomed darker with every block.

This smelt-fishing, which is a unique sort of festival confined to the Great Lakes region, begins soon after the ice goes out. Into almost every river, stream and creek that flows into most of the Great Lakes the smelts, not in mere hundreds of thousands, but in millions, suddenly swarm. They are little fish six to eight inches long, burnished silver, and with a most delicious flavor. They smell of cucumber. They were planted in the Great Lakes by accident some time before World War I, when sportsmen imported them from the Atlantic seaboard to serve as food for larger game fish in a private lake in Michigan. They got loose into the Great Lakes, where they have since multiplied beyond all belief.

And their swarming in all the creeks and rivers has given rise to a fantastic fishing festival in which tens of thousands of winter-weary sportsmen swarm like the smelts, building their bonfires along the banks, wading in the icy swollen streams and dipping like mad. When the run is at its peak, around midnight of the best of the six to 10 nights the run lasts, you can dip a bushel at a time.

"Dandy," I said, when I arrived at his front door, "it's already as cold as Greenland. By the time we get there, it will be near freezing."

"Hortense," he said, "is coming with us."

"Aw, for Pete's sake, Dandy!" I cried. "You don't know what this smelt-fishing is like. It's wading in ice water!"

"We'll just sit in the car," said Dandy smoothly. "We'll watch. We'll just occasionally get out and watch you."

"Well, of course," I said, considerably relieved. "Of course. You can come and sit by the bonfires. But I give you fair warning. You'll get pretty sick of hanging around before the night's out."

Hortense came out from the kitchen, all bundled up in sweaters under her winter coat. Dandy was done up in scarves and sweaters.

"I've read about this smelt-fishing," said Hortense. "Seen pictures of it. They get bushel baskets full."

"You sit in the back seat," yelled Dandy.

Hortense took out the plug of her hearing aid.

"We got a couple of bushel baskets," said Dandy, producing them from the hall closet.

There were four.

"Well," I exclaimed. "You've got a lot of faith in my dipping!"

I put the baskets in the trunk, along with my boots and mackinaw.

It is only an hour to the farm of Fred McLean, who invites me each spring to join his party on the stream that tumbles through his land. There were four bonfires going when we drove in the lane and around past the barn to the orchard, where the cars were parked. Fred, when he saw my companions, had me drive down to a choice position, from which Dandy and Hortense could view the fun around two of the fires.

The run was already on. In the dancing firelight, the wading sports were dipping their longhandled wiremesh dip nets, shaped like waste baskets. They would sweep them deep in the swollen stream, and up would come half a basketful of the shining, shimmering little fish.

"Get me something to sit on," directed Dandy, clambering out of the car.

Hortense chose to sit comfortably in the car.

Fred had a dip net for me, and after pulling on my waders, I headed for the stream, taking one of Dandy's four bushel baskets with me.

And for a very entertaining hour, I forgot all about Dandy.

The smelts come in spurts. When a flush of them sweeps past, you dip like mad. I had the bushel basket half full in a few minutes. So I slowed down, joining some of my fellow dippers for a rest on the bank, and renewing last year's acquaintances among them. Like the others, I took turns at stoking a bonfire for which Fred McLean had provided stacks of cordwood. I saw old Dandy circulating around, and was glad to note he was not attempting to do any dipping. Around midnight, Mrs. McLean and some other women arrived with buckets of coffee and doughnuts. It was a champion run. Everybody had their baskets, sacks, buckets and wash boilers full of smelts, and we gathered around the fires and the coffee.

Dandy, coffee cup and doughnut in hand, sought me out.

"Well!" I cried. "I'm GLAD you suggested coming. Have you enjoyed yourself?"

"I got three bushels," said Dandy.

I stared at him.

"They're in the trunk," said Dandy. "I got different fellas to dip me a few. Hortense helped me carry. There's room for your basket."

"But Dandy!" I cried. "What in the world will you do with THREE BUSHELS?"

"Oh, I can give some to my friends," said Dandy.

You can count Dandy's friends on your two elbows. That would be Hortense and me.

"Three BUSHELS!" I protested.

"As a matter of fact," said Dandy, "I'm going to use them in the garden."

"The garden?"

"Fertilizer," explained Dandy, taking a loud gulp of coffee. "I was reading in the paper that fish make a marvellous fertilizer."

"You can't use fish for fertilizer in the CITY!" I declared.

"Can't I?" said Dandy.

To which question, and to his flinty old blue eyes, there is no reply.

So I took a mug of coffee up to Hortense in the car and woke her up.

"There'll be an awful smell!" she announced, tucking in her ear plug. "The neighbors!"

"They'll enjoy the flowers," said Dandy. "Drink your coffee and go back to sleep."

Leftish

This weekend," said Joe Siswick, at lunch, "I am going to take my last desperate crack at fishing for the year 1960."

"I've already hung up my fishing tackle," I stated bleakly.

"I quit amonth ago," said Herriot.

"Oh, well," said Cooper, crumbling his roll.

"Where are you planning to go, Joe?" I enquired.

"To the cottage," said he.

"Aw, for Pete's sake," I exclaimed, "you've been fished out on that lake for years. I was there two years ago at the Boswells' and I never . . ."

"Just a minute," said Joe. "I'm not going to fish the lake. I admit I haven't got a bass out of it for five or six years. Though I remember when we first built our cottage there, you could catch bass right off the dock. Dandy bass, two, three pounds."

"It's a tragedy what we've done to our resort lakes," said Herriot.

"They're nothing but amusement parks now," agreed Cooper. "Instead of loop-the-loop, we've got 40-horse outboards dashing about."

"Okay, Joe," I demanded. "Where are you going to fish?"

Joe leaned closer, so the people at adjoining tables wouldn't hear.

"Do you know," he asked, "about that little lake one mile back of my cottage?"

"The one with the rock island in the middle?" I enquired. "Sure, I used to hunt around there years ago. A pretty little . . . "

"There's no road anywhere near it," said Joe, low. "No trail to it. It's just one of those little lost lakes back there in the bush. I don't think the natives even know of it."

"Are there fish in it?" I asked in some astonishment. For it was, in my recollection, just a lonely little pond of a lake, maybe 500 yards in diameter, set down amid some steep rocks.

Joe leaned closer and lowered his voice still more.

"Twenty years ago," he said, "my father took me in there, when I was a kid. He portaged a canoe in. And we caught strings of great big bass you wouldn't believe . . . "

"And you haven't been in since?" I protested.

"I'm not the canoe portaging type," said Joe. "But it occurred to me if I could get somebody to come with me and help carry the canoe. It's a good mile. A long carry. Over mighty rough territory . . . "

"How," said Cooper, "about the four of us? We could take turns, two by two, carrying the canoe. That would make it easy work. And when we get to the lake, we could take turns, two by two, fishing from the canoe. When the first two get a bass each, they come ashore and let the other two . . . "

In such innocence are the great adventures of this life launched.

We left in two cars, since Joe Siswick had to bring his family home after closing his cottage for the summer. I had Herriot in my car and we drove the three hours to Siswick's cottage with rapidly mounting hope.

"These little hide-away inland lakes and ponds," said Herriot, "are often gold mines. If there's fish in it, we've got to keep it strictly to ourselves."

"Not many people," I reflected, "are willing to portage a canoe a whole mile for a little fishing."

And it was a pretty lumpy old canoe that we found when we arrived at Joe's cottage. I imagine it was the one his father had portaged 20 years ago, and it had accumulated several coats of paint and soaked up a lot of water in the interval.

Joe's wife made a little fuss about us going fishing when she had all the bother and trouble of closing the cottage on this last weekend.

But we set off, around 2 p.m., carrying only two rods and one small tackle box so as not to exhaust ourselves between carries. Joe and Cooper took first carry, as Joe knew the way. Being no longer young, we decided on five-minute treks.

The route from Joe's cottage to the lake lies due north. But there are so many rocky ridges and so many little pothole swamps and gullies filled with tag alders that it is impossible to follow a straight path. When Herriot and I were carrying, Joe went

73

on ahead to scout the route so as to save us steps. It was no fun hefting that canoe.

"She weighs over a hundred," puffed Herriot.

"We should take rests," suggested Joe, after the fourth change-over, which was 20 minutes from starting point.

So we sat down, all four of us, to have a smoke for 10 minutes.

"Are we half-way yet?" asked Cooper.

"Well, not quite," said Joe. "It's a good mile."

It was a good mile. We had four more change-overs and another good rest when we came to a fairly large beaver meadow, with cedars and spruce in it, which Joe didn't recall having seen before.

"We must have got off the line," he said. "I figure we have gone too far to the right. We have to veer more leftish."

So we went around the left end of the beaver meadow, at the far end of which was a gully dense with alders. We had a tough time getting through it and up the far cliff.

"More leftish," said Joe, when we reached the rocks above.

Leftish we went, with four more change-overs and another good long rest for a smoke.

"We have to bring the canoe back out," reminded Cooper, darkly.

"We should see the lake any minute," said Joe.

And sure enough, we did. With a loud and cheery shout, Joe, walking ahead, announced he could see water through the trees.

And in no time at all, revived in spirits, we came to another steep rock, down which we carefully lowered the old canoe. And there we were on the reedy shore of as pretty a body of water as you would care to see.

"It's bigger," I said, "than I remember it from my old deer-hunting days."

"Looks fishy," said Herriot, getting the rods ready.

"I don't see that little rock island I thought was in the middle there," I added.

"Memory is a tricky thing," said Joe, shoving the canoe into the water.

I suppose it is.

Herriot took a cast from shore, just to clear his line.

Ker-splash!

A bass of three pounds took the lure before it had started to travel.

"Holy smoke!" we all yelled.

Joe and Cooper had first crack at the canoe. In five minutes, they each had a bass, and had to reluctantly paddle back in for Herriot and me to have our turn.

We were all fairly jumping with excitement.

"Man," said Joe, "if any of you so much as breathe about this to a living soul!"

"Oho, trust us!" I assured him.

"To think," he said, as he got out to make room for me, "this has been waiting all these years, and us bellyaching about the ruination of the fishing in the main lake."

Herriot got a two-pounder before I had paddled him 50 feet. I got mine, a wildcat of a three-pounder, on my second cast after Herriot handed me the rod.

"Next!" yelled Joe and Cooper, watching from shore.

I was just stepping out of the canoe when we heard a screen door slam.

We all froze.

"That sounded," said Joe, shocked, "just like a screen door slamming!"

We listened.

Then an outboard motor exploded into life.

Around the corner from us!

And then, to our consternation, around the point came Mrs. Siswick in the stern of their skiff.

"What the . . . !" said Joe.

"We . . . uh . . . " I contributed.

"I guess," said Herriot, who was the quickest-witted of us, "I guess we bore too far leftish, and came back out to the big lake."

"The fished-out lake," added Cooper, crouching hurriedly to get into the canoe for his turn.

The Fade-Out

Turn off here!" called Joe Morgan from the back seat. "Turn right."

I slowed the car.

"No, no!" cried Cooper, who shared the back seat with Joe. "Keep straight on!"

"Straight on!" said Herriot, beside me, firmly.

"Aw, listen, fellows," said Joe Morgan wearily. "I know this route like a book. You save half an hour by taking this road to the right."

"Stick to the highway." said Herriot, quietly.

"Straight on," said Cooper.

"Now, look!" declared Joe, his voice rising. "I've travelled this road a hundred times . . . "

"Awfff!" said Cooper, disgusted.

Herriot just sank a little deeper into his seat.

So I took the turn to the right.

We were just a little tired of Joe. He is one of those managing men. He had taken full charge of the expedition from the moment we left the city for the September weekend fishing. And now, on our way home, fishless, and a little fatigued with one another, as all men are on fishing trips, it was coming close to the last straw.

We hadn't gone four miles down the road to the right, which was in a pretty run-down condition, before we came to a sign:

"Construction for 12 miles."

I drew the car up beside the big sign.

"Well?" I inquired.

Nobody said anything. Cooper hummed a small tune. Herriot sat up and shoved his hat over his eyes. Joe Morgan was silent.

"I'll take the next crossroad to the left," I announced, "and get back on to the highway."

It was a dirt road, and we were well jounced up by the time we regained the concrete.

"Aha!" cried Joe, cheerily, in celebration.

We were mum.

"I'll tell you where we'll eat!" cried Joe. "I know a swell little place down here about 20 miles . . . "

Herriot turned and rested his elbow on the back of the seat.

"We'll eat," he stated "at the next restaurant we come to."

"I'll tell you what we'll have," suggested Joe enthusiastically. "How about a feed of scallops? To make up for the fish we didn't get. All these highway restaurants have scallops. We'll have scallops, and a big slather of French-fried potatoes . . ."

"I'm going to have bacon and eggs," said Cooper.

"Listen!" said Joe. "There's nothing to beat a

lovely hot dish of fried scallops!".

"Here we are!" I interrupted loudly.

For on the right appeared a very trim white restaurant with flower boxes, and quite a number of good-looking cars drawn up before it on the gravel parking space.

The place was nicely crowded when we entered. The white-clad head waitress ushered us to a table at the far end. Soft music filled the air. We sat down, and accepted the shiny menus from the waitress.

As soon as she left us, Joe stood up.

"Order me scallops, boys," he said, "and French fries. I'm going to the washroom."

When he was out of hearing, I said:

"What a guy!"

"Humph!" said Cooper.

"I'm happy," said Herriot, studying the menu, "to report that there are no scallops!"

The waitress returned, and we gave our orders. Bacon and eggs for Cooper, shrimp salad for Herriot, and grilled halibut steak for me.

"The other gentleman?" inquired the waitress.

"He can order his," I said, "when he comes back."

There really isn't much to talk about, on the way home from a fishing trip. It is best to just sit and relax. We sat looking about at the other customers, all of whom were that September weekend type, quiet and a little melancholy.

Our orders arrived.

"Where's Joe?" I asked.

Cooper and Herriot were not interested.

By the time we had our paper napkins tucked in and our knives and forks in hand, Cooper came to.

"I wonder what's keeping him?" he said. "I'll look."

There was a sign directing to the washrooms, and Cooper was gone only a moment.

"He's not there!" he said.

"Not THERE?" I protested.

"That's funny," said Herriot, and he stood up and surveyed the crowd, to see if Joe had encountered somebody he knew, and, of course, would have sat down for a chat.

"I'll go and look in the car," I said, leaving my hot halibut. "Maybe he's sick."

I looked in the car. No Joe. I walked around both ends of the building, and had a look at the back.

When I came in, I met the head waitress.

"Here's a funny thing," I said. "One of our party has disappeared. He went to the washroom, and hasn't come back."

"He's not in there?" she asked.

"No, and I went all around outside," I said. "There's no sign of him."

The head waitress gave me a curious smile.

"I THINK I know," she said, "where he might be."

At which moment, two ladies and a small girl ran out of a hallway leading to the washroom.

"There's a MAN," announced the older of the two ladies loudly, "in the women's washroom!"

"That's what I figured," said the head waitress to me, calmly. "It often happens. There's a back door to it, for the use of the kitchen staff. I'll get him out that way, to save him embarrassment."

Before I could stop her, she had gone in to the women's and a moment later, out the window, I saw Joe, all bent over, running across the parking lot and crouching into my car.

I went out and opened the car door. Joe was lying on the floor.

"Oh, oh, oh!" he moaned. "The minute I got in, I knew it was the wrong one. I jumped into a cubicle when I heard women coming through the hallway. I sat down and pulled my feet up, so they wouldn't see them. Every time I thought the coast was clear, more women came in.

"Then that little girl peeked under the swinging door of the cubicle," he said, "and yelled there was a MAN in there!"

"Joe," I said, "there are no scallops on the menu. What can I bring you out here? A sandwich? A cup of coffee?"

"Nothing!" croaked Joe. "Nothing!"

So I went back in and told Cooper and Herriot all the particulars; and we had apple pie and cheese and two cups of coffee, and enjoyed a good, long dawdly meal, the way fishermen do, after a happy weekend.

The Deceased

Some newspapermen, the lucky ones, are chained to their desks their whole lives through, like galley slaves, never getting farther than about 47 miles from their native city or town. They become moss-incrusted. No tide can stir them. They are mollusks. But they at least know what is going on in their own home city or town. They know who's alive and who's dead, for one thing.

We others, we homeless newspapermen, are condemned to roam the Seven Seas like the Flying Dutchman, and the six continents like the Wander-

ing Jew, forever journeying by luxury liner or
turbo-jet, living in palatial hotels, eating at such
places as Scott's (sole à la Scott), or Zia Theresa's
(vongolt, please), or Ma Crosby's in Villa Acuna
(quail on toast), and don't forget Money's in Bou-
logne (moules marinieres, please, the large bowl!).

And we never know what the dickens has happened in town since we were last home.

For instance:

On the street, I met F. J. Binns, Jr., and after
exchanging a few pleasantries, I inquired of Binns:

"By the way, how's Percy?"

"Percy?" asked Binns, looking startled.

"Percy Ballus." I said.

"My dear boy," said Binns. "Percy died months
ago!"

"No!"

"It must have been early last spring."

Well, there you are. It happens all the time. I
guess the best thing is not to inquire about anybody, and let it break on you gently.

But I was really sorry about Percy. Not that I
knew him intimately or could count him among my
closer friends. But he owned the most beautiful fly
rod I ever saw in my whole life. It was made by one
of those Maine hand-made fly-rod geniuses. And if
I had only known Percy had passed on, I could
have, after a decent interval of course, called his
widow and inquired if there was anything I could
do to help her dispose of his fishing tackle and
stuff. Always an unhappy problem for a widow.

And boom! Percy died months ago!

Sometimes, I could almost wish I had been a desk
man.

Well, months went by after my conversation with

Binns, and only occasionally would melancholy rec-
ollections of poor Percy Ballus rise in my mind.
Usually about this time of year, with the trout
season only a few weeks off.

You may well imagine my consternation, therefore, last Tuesday, on boarding the Winnipeg-
Montreal express and going into the club car to see,
sitting calmly reading the latest issue of Field And
Stream, whom but Percy Ballus, or his ghost, or his
double.

I stood swaying in the aisle staring incredulously
when Percy looked up, smiled delightedly, and
said:

"Why hello, Greg!"

"Percy!" I gasped. "Percy Ballus!"

"Haven't seen you in months," said Percy. "Here,
sit down!"

I needed to.

"You're looking older," remarked Percy, survey-
ing me.

"You're not," I assured him.

"Mustn't overdo it, Greg," said Percy, studying
me sharply. "You look all in."

"Oh, I get these twinges every once in a while," I
confessed. "I'll be all right in a minute."

And in a minute, I was, and Percy was happy to
inform me, after 10 minutes, that I looked my old
self.

So we launched into a most pleasant discussion of
the big events of the past couple of years since our
paths had crossed. The chief of these was Percy's
catching an ouananiche up in the Lake St. John
area that was only one ounce short of six pounds.

"Which rod," I asked indifferently, "were you
using?"

Yep. It was the one.

"You want to take great care of a rod like that." I warned him. "A six-pound ouananiche on a little rod like that . . ."

"Oh, I take care of it, don't worry," said Percy.

"You wouldn't want anything to happen," I reflected, "to a rod like that."

As soon as I got back to Toronto, I looked up F. J. Binns, Jr. I didn't telephone him. I went straight to his office.

"I thought you told me," I declared, "that Percy Ballus was dead!"

"So he is," said Binns.

"The heck he is!" I cried hotly. "I ran into him on the Winnipeg-Montreal train on Tuesday!"

"Percy?"

"Yes, Percy! And he's as alive as you or I. Aliver! He's the picture of health. I bet he will outlast the both of us."

"Well, now," protested Binns, "that's the strangest thing! I was SURE he was dead. I remember . . ."

And Binns went into a huddle with himself.

"I remember," he declared firmly, "reading that Percy was dead in a paper out West, last spring some time. Let's see. I was in Lethbridge. No, it was Drumheller! Let me see. Maybe it was in B.C. Yes, it could have been in Nelson or Cranbrook that I read in the paper that Percy was dead. One of those towns . . ."

"Aw, Binns," I groaned, "you've got to be more careful. You can't go around saying people are dead."

"Look," said Binns. "I'm a travelling man. I'm not one of the executives of this firm, who sits chained to his desk his whole life through, like a galley slave. They know who's dead and who isn't.

But I'm a travelling man. I roam this country like the Flying Dutchman, or the Wandering Jew, forever and ever, riding in stuffy trains, bumping from airfield to airfield on local airlines, humping over prairie and mountain in rented jalopies. I'm hardly ever home. How do I know who's dead?"

"Well, you said Percy . . ."

"We can all be mistaken," said Binns.

So I left F. J. Binns, Jr., with a due sense of reproach.

But would you like a small bet?

I bet you dollars to doughnuts that Percy Ballus smashes that rod this very season!

The Finger

The Mudcat Lake Cottage Opening and Closing Corporation, Inc., is definitely not a large organization.

As a matter of fact, just the four of us constitute it: Herriot, Cooper, Pete Denison and I.

I suppose I should have itemized Pete Denison first, because it is his cottage up on Mudcat Lake, that we open and close each year. He is, in a sense, the chairman of the board.

He called us together last week for the annual spring meeting of the corporation. Lunch. Dutch, of course. There are no directors' fees.

"O.K., boys," he said, at the conclusion of the meeting, which consisted of finnan haddie, creamed, with peas. "Friday. We go in Herriot's car. Clark brings the meat. Cooper the vegetables, including salad. I bring the canned goods. O.K.?"

We voted O.K. And Denison, being an insurance man, always on the warpath after scalps, excused himself and headed for the exit.

We watched him, affectionately, until he was out of earshot.

"Remember," said Cooper, "the canned goods he brought last year?"

"Well, after all," I reasoned, "it's his cottage."

"Yes," said Herriot. "But what do we go up for? We go up to OPEN it! To take off the shutters. To climb up on the roof and take off that board, with the big rock on top of it, that he covers the chimney with. To haul his boat out of the boathouse . . ."

"Aw," said Cooper, "and sweep all the dead leaves and mouse nests out of the rooms. And yank the mattresses out of that storage closet he's got. And make the beds . . ."

"It's a small price," I declared, "for the fun we have."

"There's just one little thing I'd like to mention," said Cooper. "Last year, you recollect, Pete had a sprained ankle. Didn't he? And it didn't improve until we had done all the work."

"Hmmmm," said Herriot and I.

"The year BEFORE," said Cooper, "he had his arm in a sling. Didn't he? And he didn't get it out of the sling until all the shutters were off, all the mattresses hauled out of that cupboard . . ."

"Hmmm-mmm!" said Herriot and I.

"And the year before THAT," cried Cooper, "he had that sore finger. Remember? All done up in a bandage as big as a banana. And it was while we were out bobbing mudcats that the bandage slipped off. Remember?"

"Weeeeel," I said, "Pete is a kind of dramatic sort of guy."

"Fine," said Cooper. "But I suggest we get dramatic this time. I propose that the three of us all arrive with some disability. I'll have my finger done up in a bandage. You, Greg, have your arm in a sling. And Herriot . . ."

"I've got to drive," reminded Herriot.

"You," said Cooper, "will come all over faint, when we get there, and you'll have to lie down for two hours."

The thing appealed to us.

Mind you, Pete Denison is a nice guy. But there is no doubt that he can think up more ways for other people to do things than anybody in our social circle. I guess it is due to the insurance business. After thinking about all those accidents, and all those unexpected and often untimely deaths that he has to talk about to his clients all day, I suppose a man becomes a little careful of himself, and doesn't like to exhaust his energy.

The thing appealed to us, as I say. So when Friday arrived, I had my arm all done up in a sling when Herriot called to pick me up. In my other hand I carried the parcel of ham steaks, T-bone steaks and the three pounds of hamburger.

When we picked up Cooper, he came out with his basket of vegetables and salad greens in one hand, and his bag in the other. And he had a finger on BOTH hands all done up in large white bandages.

"Isn't that overdoing it a little?" I suggested.

"No," cried Cooper, joyously. "My wife asked me to put the electric iron away. She had forgotten to turn it off. I picked it up in my TWO hands, instead of by the handle . . ."

And he held up the two bandaged fingers.

"I can still," he said, getting in the car, "manage a cigarette between my thumb and first finger. How's

86

your arm?"

"Aw," I said, "it's as good as can be expected, after me falling down the cellar stairs."

"Good," said Herriot. "You both sound authentic."

We picked up Pete Denison last. He came out with his valise and the usual paper bag with two or three cans of beans and a couple of cans of peaches.

"Holy smoke!" he said, glancing in at Cooper and me, our bandages in excellent visibility.

He was without any outward sign of injury.

"I'm O.K.!" mentioned Herriot.

"Thank goodness for that," said Pete. "I've had a couple of weak spells during the morning, and I had half a mind to call you boys and put the trip off."

"No, no!" all three of us cried. "We'll manage."

I should explain to you why we are so keen on Mudcat Lake. The reason is, it is full of mudcats. And the two seasons during which mudcats are in their prime are May and September.

You gentlemen sportsmen who go after the trout, the salmon, the bass, the walleye and the muskellunge may look down your noses at the mudcat. But if you will keep your eyes open, you will see your guides, at $10 or even $15 a day, after faithfully propelling you around the sporting wilds, serving you a shore dinner of trout, salmon, bass, walleye or muskellunge. But what do they eat? Mudcats. The most delectable of all fresh-water fish.

Mudcats are the ugliest of God's creatures. Their eyes are where most creatures keep their ears. Their eyes are pale grey. They have snaky whiskers that dangle wetly on either side of their flat, scow-shaped snouts. You don't catch them on hooks.

You catch them on bobs or gobs of worms, about the size of golf balls. You don't fish for them in the light of day. You bob for them in the dark of night, dangling the ball of worms over the side of the punt in two or three feet of muddy, swampy, back-bay water, full of lily pads. With their wide mouths, they suck in the ball. You hoist. You hold your mudcat over the galvanized washtub in the punt. It lets go. And falls into the washtub.

"Away we go!" cried Pete Denison, easing in beside Herriot and slamming the car door.

"EEEEEE-YOW!" he roared.

He had slammed his finger in the crack.

So I took off my sling, Cooper took off his bandages, we hustled Pete back into his apartment and bandaged him up.

And we were two hours late arriving at Mudcat Lake, but not too late for a snack, around 11 p.m., of skinned mudcats fried in deep fat.

Mmmmmmm!

The Observation

My nephew, Charlie, the salesman, often flatters me by asking my advice. I know nothing about salesmanship, and I tell him so. I hate to steer kids up blind alleys, the kind I love to explore.

"You're daft, Uncle Greg," agreed Charlie. "But often, you daft people have a sort of roundabout way of looking at things."

"Indeed?" I said. "What's the problem this time?"

"Do you know an old buzzard by the name of Parlone? Thomas B. Parlone?"

"I've heard of him," I admitted. "Mining, isn't

he? Rich old gentleman?"

"Rich, and hard, and cold," said Charlie. "He buys about half a million dollars' worth of machinery every year."

"That would be a nice order," I remarked.

"My firm," said Charlie, who has been with it about 16 months, "have been trying to get to him for 10 years. As a joke, they sent me to see him this morning. And do you know what!"

"What?"

"His secretary is my old Sunday-school teacher, Miss Bell!"

"Then . . . ?"

"I got in to see him!" cried Charlie. "Thomas B. Parlone! Miss Bell just walked me in and said: 'Here's a young fellow wants to speak to you.'"

"I hope you were able to rise to the occasion," I said.

"It was ghastly," groaned Charlie. "I was so bewildered, I didn't know what to say. I just blurted out that I knew he bought an awful lot of machinery, and we had an awful lot to sell."

He buried his face in his hands.

"You mean to say . . . ?" I gasped.

"I couldn't remember a thing," said Charlie. "All the patter I had learned. All the line. All the calm approach. All about the service we offer. I just stood there and blithered."

"Too bad," I consoled, "to lose a break like that Miss Bell."

"Oh, I haven't lost it," exclaimed Charlie. "The old buster said he was too involved at the moment to think of machinery. He told me to come back a week today, at 10. And be prepared to show him what we have to offer."

"Good boy!"

"What I think I'll do," said Charlie, "is take one of our senior men along with me."

"Don't BREATHE it to any senior man!" I shouted. "My dear young man, this is the chance of your life. Make a sale nobody else could make? Why, it will be the making of you."

"But it's big stuff, Uncle Greg," explained Charlie. "And I don't know enough about machinery yet."

"Listen, son," I counselled. "Old Mr. Parlone probably knows more about machinery than your seniorest senior. He uses it. He doesn't merely sell it. You take your catalogues and lists along and show them to the old boy. By the way, what's he like?"

"Cold, hard," said Charlie, reflecting. "Kind of grizzled and brindled. A harsh sort of red face."

"Drink?"

"No, kind of rough red, scrubbed sort of, with veins on his cheek bones."

"High blood pressure?" I asked.

"Not on your life. Quiet, cold, icy. His blood is probably congealed, if anything."

"What was his office like?

"How do you mean?" asked Charlie.

"Well, heck," I said, "the first thing a salesman does is size up his man by the things visible. Listen: observation is the first requisite in any profession. Doctors, lawyers, detectives, everybody has to develop the power of observation. It's the secret of everything. What was Mr. Parlone's office like? Plain or fancy?"

"Kind of rich," said Charlie.

"What sort of pictures did he have on the wall?" I inquired. "Pictures of his wife and family? Pictures of his deceased rivals in business? Pictures of prominent statesmen? A good salesman can tell at a swift glance whether his prospect is a family man, an ambitious man, a vain man . . . "

"The only thing I noticed," said Charlie, lamely, "was a stuffed fish."

"A FISH!" I exclaimed. "What kind of a fish, Charlie?"

"Maybe a trout," he said. "Maybe a bass."

"Aw, Charlie!" I wailed. "You had the man doubly in your clutches! Miss Bell, and then this stuffed fish!"

"There were some rods," recollected Charlie, "leaning in a corner. Rods in tin tubes, with leather caps on the tubes."

"Fly rods!" I cried. "It was a trout, I bet. A stuffed trout. How big was it?"

Charlie held his hands apart.

About a five-pounder.

"Charlie, boy," I announced. "You have wasted your young life on rugby, hockey, golf and skiing. But by a week today, you are going to be a trout fisherman."

I gave him an intensive course in the art of angling.

I made him come to my house every evening, while I went over my rods, lines, reels, tackle and flies. I made him read the elementary books on the art, like Lord Grey's Fly Fishing, and study through Haig-Brown's The Western Angler. I drilled him so he could identify two or three dozen of the familiar flies like the Par Belle, the Montreal, March Brown, Black Gnat and Grizzly King. And on Friday, I got Dr. Alan Secord to invite both of us up to his trout pond for an evening's practical demonstration of the art.

"How long has this been going on?" asked young

Charlie in a happy daze, as we came in, at dark.

"About 2,000 years," said Dr. Secord. "The Roman writer, Aelian, refers to fly fishing in the First Century, A.D."

For Charlie had caught on to fly-casting in less than 20 minutes; and cast with skill by dark; and had eight trout besides.

We talked fishing all the way home in the car.

"I feel better about seeing Mr. Parlone, Monday," said Charlie.

"Remember!" I warned. "The minute you come in the door, and before you even sit down, say: 'Where did you get that trout, Mr. Parlone?' in a tone of profound astonishment."

"Right!" said Charlie.

He promised to phone me the minute his interview with Mr. Parlone was over.

He didn't. He came straight to see me.

"He's invited me," cried Charlie, "to come up with him next week to a lake near one of his mines. We have to fly in. It's FULL of four- and five-pounders!"

"Fine, but how about the order?" I cut in. "The machinery!"

"Oh, he ordered about five carloads," said Charlie. "But this lake . . . "

"Can you get away from the office?"

"The boss says I can take a month if I like. Now, this lake . . . "

Daft?

Who's daft?

Chum

Dickinson who has the cottage directly across the channel from ours came over in his outboard.

He is not the sort of visitor you have to go down to the dock to welcome, so I just sat.

"Can I speak to you a minute?" he called.

"Come on up," I invited.

He came up on the veranda.

"Anybody here?" he asked.

"Just us," I said.

He went into the living room and looked around.

"I don't want anybody to overhear," he said when he came back out. "Did you ever hear of chumming?"

"Chumming?" I checked.

"Do you ever see a publication of the federal fisheries department," he asked, "called Trade News? It's a monthly."

"Yes, I've seen it," I said.

"In the last issue," said Dickinson, speaking low, "which I happened to pick up at the Board of Trade when I was having lunch there yesterday, I saw this article on chumming. Down on the Atlantic coast, when they are fishing for tuna, they net a whole boatload of small fish, like herring, and chop them up. That's called chum."

"Chum," I appreciated, for I am very fond of herring in any form.

"Then they dump this chopped-up chum overboard as they cruise along in their boat," went on Dickinson, "making a sort of trail."

"Is it legal?" I enquired.

"Certainly," said Dickinson, "it's professional.

Well, when a school of tuna comes along and picks up this trail of chum, they come boiling along after it, in the wake of the fishermen's boat. And when the fishermen see the tuna breaking water behind them, they throw out their lines baited with whole herring, and that's the way they hook the tuna."

"I'd like to try it some time," I admitted.

"You can," said Dickinson, lowering his voice and glancing around at the living room door for fear anybody might be eavesdropping.

"When?" I asked.

"Now," said Dickinson. "Right here. Right in our own bay."

"Aw," I protested.

"In this article," said Dickinson, in a whisper, "it said that it was the same principle as the trick used by freshwater fishermen who punch holes in a can of sardines, tie a line on to it and drag it along the bottom of a lake. This lays a trail. And all the fish cruising around the lake pick it up and come to the point where the fishermen have dumped three or four freshly punctured sardine cans to sink in one spot, at the end of the trail."

"Holy smoke!" I said, sitting up.

"All the fish in the lake congregate around these sardine cans," hissed Dickinson. "And we, who are the only ones who know where the cans are, drop our lines down into a regular congregation of fish!"

I lowered my voice and stood up.

"Where can we get some sardines?" I whispered.

"I brought up a dozen tins of the cheap ten cent kind," replied Dickinson, "when I came last night."

"Then what are we waiting for?" I asked, starting for the steps.

"Don't be a darn fool," said Dickinson sharply. "There are 15 cottages in full view of us where we

95

sit right here. There's five more I've counted that can see us if we start laying the trail in daylight. What we've got to do is decide where we'll lay the trail of chum, and to what spot. Then, as soon as it's dark, we'll rig a couple of punctured sardine cans on lines and drag them . . ."

We decided that a spot straight in front of us, between both our cottages, would be best for the round up, the grand congregation, or fish corral.

We agreed that we would lay two trails of sardines, one from either end of the bay, zig-zagging towards the central spot in front of our cottages.

And there, in the deep hole, we would end both trails by cutting loose the punctured cans we had dragged, and also drop down three or four full cans, freshly punctured so as to leak their succulent juices into the surrounding depths.

That was Saturday last.

We laid two trails between 9 and 10 p.m. We dropped five cans into the chosen spot, plus the two decoys we had dragged.

Sunday was a tough day for Dickinson and me. There were a lot of boats swishing about the bay and channel all day, several neighbors paid one or the other of us friendly calls, so we decided it would be unwise to do any exploring of the area before dark. You may recall it blew a gale Sunday evening starting about supper time: so we didn't get out.

Monday, many of the weekending men had left and only the women would be watching, if any. So Dickinson and I went out very casually in our outboards and trolled some deep lures round the chummed area.

We got nothing.

We tried in the afternoon, and again at dusk.

No luck.

"We'll lay another trail or two," said Dickinson.

So Monday night, after dark, we dragged not one but two punctured sardine cans on each of the zig-zag routes we had chosen to draw the fish from the far ends of the bay. We even put in a few extra zigs and a zag or two.

Tuesday, I noticed the Flemings, who are the third cottage from ours, hauling up their water pipe that pumps water into their tank at the back of the cottage. They had the boys from the marine gas station down the lake helping them.

I dropped over.

"Must be a fish stuck in our pipe," said Mr. Fleming. "The water tastes fishy."

Dickinson came over around ten in his outboard, all ready to do some trolling with me.

"Hello." he said. "The Flemings are pulling up their pipe too, eh?"

"Too?" said I.

"Sure," said Dickinson. "Over on my side, the Martins and the Andersons are busy hauling in their water pipes. Got a lot of fellows from down at the Landing helping them."

"I wonder what's the matter?" I asked.

We got in my boat and trolled around the secret spot for half an hour without result, and then I, being at the outboard end, steered a run down the channel a way.

We met a Mr. Stevens in his outboard coming up.

"Hey," he hailed us, "have you seen any of the boys from the Landing working up here?"

"They're at the Flemings or the Martins or the Andersons," I yelled back.

"I've got a dead fish stuck in my water pipe," called Stevens, "and I got to get them to help me haul in the pipe . . . "

I ran alongside his boat.

"Dead fish, eh?" I said.

"Well, it tastes like sardines, sort of," said Stevens.

"Oh," said I.

"Oh," said Dickinson.

"So long," said I.

I ran the boat out into the quiet middle of the bay.

"I guess," I said to Dickinson, "we'd better haul up our water pipes too, eh? It might look suspicious if we didn't."

The boys from the Landing charged us each $8 for time and labor.

And by the way, Dickinson and I figure there weren't any fish IN the bay at this particular time.

Maybe they had left.

The Jewels

In the day coach between Melville and Saskatoon, I had to take an aisle seat. The man next to the window beside me gave me a nudge as soon as I had slid my bag and coat up to the baggage rack.

I looked at him.

He nodded toward the seats across the aisle from us and winked.

Across the aisle, the seats had been turned to face each other. Facing the way the train was going sat two large men with solid expressions. Facing them were two youths who glanced at me as I glanced at them. Their expressions were defiant.

Then I noticed that they were handcuffed together.

"Hmmm," I said to the man beside me.

"Too bad, eh?" he replied quietly. "I guess the cops are taking them on to Prince Albert."

To spare the youngsters embarrassment, I turned in my seat slightly to chat with my seat mate.

"There," I remarked, "but for the grace of God, goes any of us."

"Just what I have been sitting here thinking," said my seat mate. He was a big man. I think he was a prosperous farmer, or maybe a small-town dealer in farm machinery and trucks. A pleasant, affable big fellow. "Did you ever do anything that might have landed you . . . ?

And he nodded in the direction of the youths.

"I recollect one time," I confessed, "I was in a movie theatre line-up for the ticket window, and I had my sweetheart with me. A big, well-dressed lug calmly pushed in line ahead of me. I protested. He gave me a contemptuous shove and laughed. There was a scuffle. He threw me half-way across the street. If I had had a pistol that night, I know in my heart I would have shot him in the guts!"

I turned hot at the very memory.

"But you didn't have a gun," smiled the big man. "I'm in a worse fix. I once planned a robbery."

"Well, now!" I protested.

"Yes," he said. "I not only planned a robbery, I broke into a man's house."

"Oh, come!" I scoffed.

The big fellow hunkered down a little bit to chat more confidentially with me.

"I was 19," he said. "It was in the worst days of the depression, 1936, when the country was crawling with kids my age wandering like hoboes all over

Canada. I had picked up with another young fellow about three years older than me. We hitched our way from the West, here, to Montreal. We were trying to get to Halifax, thinking we might get a job on a boat.

"In Montreal, we did a lot of panhandling, picked up odd jobs, slept in box cars when we couldn't get into a mission or a police station. One night, we went out into the residential areas ringing door bells, pretending to want snow-shovelling jobs, but really looking for dimes and quarters. You can imagine."

I looked at the big chap. He was flushed with confession.

"We came to this small, neat house," he went on, "back in from the street a ways. It needed its snow shovelled. When we got up on the steps, we could see in a window. An elderly man was sitting under a light. I can see him yet. He had a black box in front of him on another chair. Out of the box he had taken a smaller box, like a little black jewel case. He was examining it intently. My chum and I never made a move. We watched."

"Nobody else in the room?" I suggested.

"We watched," said my seat mate. "The old boy sat there, gloating over what he was seeing. He would touch the jewels. He would pick something small and glittering out of the box and put it back in. I could hardly breathe. You never saw such a scene of greedy gloating as that old man under the lamp light. As we watched, he would put one small box back in the big black box and take out another little box, open it and stare, and pick things out and inspect them lovingly.

"I guess my chum and I must have watched him 20 minutes, fascinated, before we signalled each other to go for a walk and talk things over.

" 'Jewels,' " said my chum.

" 'Diamonds,' " I agreed. "Rubies. I could see them glinting."

"So my chum and I decided to go back to the lodging house we had 25-cent beds in and plan the job. We spent the whole next day figuring and planning. Everything depended on how many people were in the house with the old man. The only way to find out was to watch the house. Before dark—it was about this time of year, too—we went back and walked up and down the street with snow shovels we had borrowed from the lodging house, pretending to be looking for jobs. The old man came home about 6 p.m. He let himself in with a key. Nobody else came for an hour. About 7:30 p.m. we went up on his steps.

"There he was, sitting under the lamp again, with the large black box open on the chair before him. And he was sitting gazing into one of the smaller boxes, just like the night before. If there was anybody else in the house, we figured they would show up, sooner or later. We had decided to watch for about half an hour, long enough for anybody to appear. We were very quiet, in the shadow of the little veranda on the steps . . ."

My seat mate was a little breathless with his tale.

"At 8:30," he said. "I hated the sight of that old miser so, gloating over his treasures at a time like that, with the whole world starving and kids like us wandering, that I felt I was doing the decent thing to go in and rob him of his jewels. What good were they to him? And he sat there, by the hour, taking those little boxes out . . ."

"You went in, then?" I urged.

"We rang his bell. He came to the door. We asked

him if he wanted his snow shovelled. He said no, and as he started to close his door, my chum and I stepped in and shoved."

"Did you hurt him?" I asked.

"We pushed him aside. He was quite an old man. 'Hey, now, boys!' he hollered out.

"We dashed into the room and grabbed the box. Do you know what was in those little boxes?"

"Jewels?" I guessed.

"Trout flies!" shouted my seat mate, so that across the aisle the four looked up startled. "Trout flies, hundreds of them, all neatly arranged in the little boxes . . . "

"What did you do?" I begged.

"We ran," said my seat mate. "We just bumped past the old boy and ran. That night, I figured it was a kind of miracle for me. I gave my chum the slip and came West. I went to the war when it came along in a couple of years and grew up. But it was a narrow squeak, eh?"

So we got to Saskatoon, looking a little strangely at the two lads sitting across from us with the sullen faces.

The Purist

Anglers are divided into two broad classes. There are those who fish for fish, and don't much care how they get them—worms, frogs, leeches, hunks of liver, gang hooks, plugs, jigs, sniggling hooks, nets, spears, dynamite.

Then there is the other class—the elite.

The fly fisherman, with his eight-foot, four-ounce fly rod, that delicate wand. The new-fangled spinning enthusiast, with his fragile rod and nylon monofilament line and tiny jewelled lures. The light-tackle expert with the bait-casting rod who, with a flick of the wrist, can hit a dinner plate with his lure at 50 feet every cast.

It is from these, the elite, that the purists are drawn. The purists are those who, driven by inner compulsions of the kind that made the great martyrs, refine and refine their methods of fishing until they feel so superior to all other fishermen that they can hardly bear the company of their fellow-men.

They buy lighter and lighter rods, more and more fragile leaders, tinier and tinier flies and lures. So immense is their personal sense of sportsmanship that they often end up by not going fishing at all, but just sit alone, like God, thinking about it.

I had been fly-fishing for about 12 years before I began to get delusions of purism. In a London, England, tackle shop dedicated to purists, I saw some dry flies so tiny, so fragile, so captivating that I bought 10 dozen of them. These wonderful flies you do not cast into the water, like common trout flies. No. You cast them ON the water, and they must float.

You do not chuck them into the water at random, hoping a trout will see them. No. You go and sit by the river bank and wait until a trout dimples, as they say, on the surface. Then you stalk that trout: that one trout. You PRESENT the delicate little dry fly to him; cast it upstream six feet above him; float it magically over him. And up he comes to it.

Becoming a purist is a mysterious business. It happens to you overnight. It can happen in a twinkling. One minute you are an ordinary, common angler. The next, you are a purist. You feel holy.

When I got home to Canada, having doted on the new flies all the way across on the ship, I immediately announced my conversion to all my erstwhile friends and formerly boon companions. We went fishing together, as usual. But I fished my way, and they fished theirs. They waded and punted and sloshed around, furiously thrashing the stream with their vulgar flies. But I—I sat serene by the riverside, awaiting the dimple or rise of a trout.

Presently I noted a more respectful attitude on the part of my friends. They began to treat me with a certain reverence. Guides tipped their hats to me. Villagers came to their doors, when I walked by, streamward, with my dry-fly rod and tackle. The rewards of purism were beginning to be manifest.

The next stage was when my friends and even strangers began coming to sit at a distance in the bushes or on the meadows to watch the Master at work.

There was one splendid pool on our river called Sing's Spring. There, one lovely afternoon, I had detected a large trout rising. I crept up and knelt as near the stream as I dared and began presenting one of the seductive tiny dry flies to it. I was happy to observe some villagers on the far bank, respectfully watching from the underbrush. And a punt with three of my friends came upstream and reverently pulled into the bank to wait and watch. I false cast, and fed out my line. I laid the fly on the water.

Unknown to me, some cows, mostly heifers, had wandered over the meadows behind me. And perceiving the curious hunched figure down by their favorite waterhole, they approached with caution.

I picked off my line and made some more false casts in the air, to lengthen line.

The youngest heifer, naturally, was the boldest. She, with head lowered, sneaked up closer and closer.

I did not even hear her breathe.

My back cast reached far back; the forward cast began with power. My line and leader swished past the heifer. The fly caught her square in the left ear.

I felt the jolt.

I felt a violent jerk and a wild pull.

I leaped to my feet. The heifer, all her friends leading, dashed madly for the open fields. I followed, rod tip high.

Now, all I had to do was stop and point the darn rod, and let her snap the fragile leader. It wouldn't hold a pound.

But a purist is not of this world.

Wildly I followed, while faint in my ears rang the cheers and encouragement of my friends in the punt, and the villagers amid the underbrush.

It takes courage to be a purist when your friends, and the villagers, and the old guide, are constantly inquiring how I'm doing lately, and how's prices at the stock yards?

I haven't that much courage.

To the satisfaction of my friends, I have become an ordinary average fish hog once more.

106

A Sportsman Is One

The true sportsman is one who not only will not show his own father where the best fishing hole is, but will deliberately direct him to the wrong one.

Sportsmen, it seems to me, are the last remaining receptacles of the true human spirit. The natural man, the man who survived through countless aeons of tribulation such as the Ice Age and sundry plagues of smallpox, not to mention prophets priests and kings, must have been a sportsman; by which I mean a creature given to hunting, fishing, carousing, chasing and loafing. The only survivals of that natural man in this final era of the decline of the human species, are the sportsmen. Sure, it's the decline. We show all the vices common to decline, like horses gnawing their stable timber or cattle eating bones. And what a lot of nasty gnawing is going on all over the world nowadays, as with every utterance, philosophic, social, governmental, the nature of man is being blasphemed.

We are multiplying enormously, which is another symptom of decline. When nature grows sick of a species, as she did of the passenger pigeon or the dinosaur or any of the things we find in the limestone, she multiplies them incredibly, as if in a last vain hope. Then the plague takes them. A plague does not work up much virulence on a lone hermit. But it goes big in crowded London. In terror, the survivors huddle together. But the engendered plague germs are so many, so strong, that even the sportsmen among the dinosaurs and passenger pigeons are wiped out to the last one.

Not that I am fond of sportsmen. Every time I

see in my morning paper the one column cut of the gent in a derby hat and a cold cheesy face with the lines "Well Known Sportsman Passes," I know at once that the gent was one of those who never attended a race or other sporting event except on a free pass, and never bet on a horse until the owner had tipped him off that the race was a benefit for the jockeys. I hold no brief for sportsmen. I think they are the craftiest, most self-seeking, most devious, most nefariously ingenious of men. But I believe them to be the natural man. And I prefer their company to all other.

This story of the maskinonge that undressed me has little to do with the above sentiments except to reveal, in some mystical way even I do not understand, though I tell it, the deeper nature of sportsmen.

The middle of October is the legal closing in Ontario of the maskinonge season. I do not deny that certain sportsmen, notably Indians and native sons, continue to take this king of freshwater fishes all through the year both by sporting methods as well as by spears, nets, pitchforks and dynamite. But those of us who, by reason of the vices aforementioned such as conscience or social sense or lack of opportunity, are bound by the law, regard the maskinonge fishing of mid October to be the most royal angling of the whole year, befitting the close of all fishing; a sort of Wagnerian fourth act upon which the curtain falls, the theatre of our sport is darkened, and we creep home to hang up our rods in a cool dry closet.

In mid October, the shores of the rocky maskinonge lakes are glorious with color. The days are short and full of vim. Hale winds blow. The chill in the air wakes in our subconscious the age old instinct to fare forth to slay and fill the cave with hams and skins against the fated winter. Our blood sings.

And along the hard shores, amid the clefts of rocks, in the cold shadow of sunken logs, that tiger of freshwater fish, that lithe jade green lurker, compounded of steel springs and frenzy—the maskinonge—awaits us. Twenty, thirty pounds he goes, commonly. Sixty pounds he goes in the Lake of the Woods; but that is heaven and not for such as we. Eight, twelve, sixteen pounds he really goes, for most of us who go plugging for him in the tapestried aisle of mid October.

All summer long, the maskinonge have lain secret in the weed beds scattered all over the lakes. But when the frost comes and the weeds die and rot and fill the water with a stinking, the muskies creep shoreward, towards the rocks and gravel beaches where the water is less fouled. There, in two, three, four feet of water, they wait until the sludge of vegetable death subsides and the waters clear. And there, along the shore, we, creeping in Indian paddled canoes and chucking our grotesque painted wooden plugs from our short, clever rods, find him.

Ah, he has no depths to sound. Under him, the rocky bottom. Beside him, rocks and shallows. There is but one element that beckons him. As he feels the sting of hooks as he senses the dread snare of line challenging that liberty which to a fish must be all in all, he leaps. Not one of those pretty up and down, in and out leaps for which the bass is so justly famous. But a savage, mad, oblique, any-old way leap that will carry him sliding and skidding across the surface a distance of twenty feet. And shaking and fighting every foot of the way, he boils, leaps, jerks, furiously exerting every ounce of his steely energy in every possible direction at once.

And to him who holds the lithe rod to which all this fury is fastened, comes a great timidity; a great, weakly-smiling, pale-jawed sense of terror. It must be the contrasts of sport that addict us. The sudden explosion of the grouse amid the frosty calm. The bound of a deer after the long patient stalk. The savage boil of a muskie to break the rhythmic monotony of the cast, cast, cast. Oh, lovely spirit-jolting shock of sport.

Jimmie Frise, that insufferable and inescapable cartoonist to whom I have been linked by Fate in as happily a misspent life as falls to any man, was successfully commissaried by me to our favorite muskie water for the closing day of the season. It is quite a trick to get cartoonists anywhere. Their favorite condition is heels on the table, *chez lui.* But dawn of closing day rose dull and soft, and Jimmie and I joined forces with an American gentleman who was staying at the hotel, a muskie addict fifteen per cent over-proof, an elderly man by the name of Mr. Scholtz from Pittsburg who carried around seven hundred dollars' worth of rods and tackle; and his guide was Old Noah. Jim's guide was Abe, as usual. Mine was Scotty Hoggarth, a Caledonian from Peebles who was married to an Indian and who was equally fluent in the Scottish and the Ojibwa.

Scotty is perhaps the greatest guide in the world. Both of us think so. As we creep silently along the shore, forty feet out, with nary a sip from the paddle as Scotty handles it, and nary a scrape or a dunt from boot of me, Scotty looks at a spot on the edge of the shore, and so great is his art, I place my lure exactly in the spot he was looking at.

"It's a forrrm of mesmerism," explains Scotty, whenever we marvel at this wonder. "I stare at the spot. It is, obviously, the best spot. I stare and stare. And then you cast, sputt, square into that verra spot. It's een-credible. No wonder we get so many fush."

And this soft, dull October day, with the shores like a faded old Paisley shawl for color, and a fitful little wind ruffling the water amid the rocky islands and channels, Scotty and I had the luck. The three canoes of us proceeded in follow-my-leader order, Mr. Scholtz first, with Old Noah humped darkly over the paddle and Mr. Scholtz with his beautiful tackle and clever fore-arm, casting three times a minute, smoothly, rhythmically; fifty yards behind him, covering the same water, I with Scotty; fifty yards behind me, Jimmie and Abe, in a deep Ojibwa silence.

Scotty and I are vocal anglers. We chat. We exclaim and we debate. We tell long tales and wonders. Whiles, we exhort the fish. We dare them to come on. Give us a chance, we defy them. Scare the both of us.

And forty minutes after starting, our exhortations had the desired effect when a ten-pounder met my plug almost before it touched the water. In a rush like a rugby player getting under the ball, the muskie plunged and met the red and white lure. I struck back. The muskie came straight for the canoe, plunging, slashing, insane. And for ten blazing minutes, I was back where all men belong— about ten thousand, twenty thousand years. Back of all piety and deceit, back of all that veneer the first year psychology students speak of. Veneer, what an ugly, lucid word.

And in due time, the fury passes; the muskie,

heavy, fain, is drawn alongside by weak wrists and thumping pulses; and Scotty, very still, very tartany of face and broadswordish of expression, makes a clean sweeping draw with the cleek, as he calls my telescopic gaff hook, and hauls the thudding monster inboard.

Of course Scholtz and Jimmie have ceased fire to watch the battle. That is the etiquette of fishing in parade. And they come alongside to admire the jade beastie and, if I mistake not, to christen it.

Now, in this lovely October morning, I was clad in garments that are of importance to the tale. I wore plus fours and jacket of a bright rusty red Harris tweed. And under the jacket, contrasting with it so sharply that all men would remember it, a yellow sweater with sleeves.

With sleeves.

Within another half hour, as the result of our continued incantations, another and a bigger muskie boiled savagely to my lure, and Jimmie and Scholtz had the pleasure of suspending activities while, with triumphant cries and tumult of victory, Scotty cleeked for me a thirteen-pounder. We all adjourned for lunch on a rocky point, where the guides gralloched and quartered and cooked my ten-pounder for luncheon. I was, by luncheon end, something of a pain to both my good companions, neither of whom all morning had so much as seen a swirl. And Scotty, I have no doubt, was something duodenal to Old Noah and Abe, as they finished up what was left of leviathan.

At any rate, through narrowed eyes, Scholtz and Jimmie must have had a good look at me as I stood forth on the rocks, in my red tweed and bright yellow sweater, informing them:

"I now have my limit of two muskies. But for the

afternoon, gentlemen, I shall keep my position between you, and cast for bass. If any muskie is so disrespectful of the law as willfully to attack my lure, I can do no more than release him, after he is subdued."

And we embarked, and set forth, full fed, in the hazy afternoon, along lovelier Paisley shawl shores than ever, I contemplating the good humor of God who should not only create small cocky men, but on top of that should permit them to catch the muskies. And my two friends extended their intervals to seventy-five yards either side of me.

Within twenty minutes of starting, I rose, hooked, hand-landed and set free a muskie of seven pounds. Less than a half hour later, I rose and dittoed another of about six pounds. By this time, I was conscious of the almost steady regard of my two friends. They would take their eyes off me long enough to make their cast. Then, as they reeled in, they would turn their heads and stare balefully in my direction. Then look away long enough to select the next spot, and make the cast.

And Scotty and I, aware that this was one of the classic hours of our lives, were suiting the occasion with words and music. We thought up all manner of discussions as to the true characteristics of an angler. Of the psychic power the genuine angler has over fish. But it was not to hear our jibes that Scholtz and Jimmie turned their heads like automatons towards us, one ahead and one behind. It was to see us catch muskies.

It was mid afternoon, and I grew warm. I laid down my rod. Whipped off my jacket. Skinned off my yellow sweater. Tossed it behind me onto the lunch basket. Donned my red tweed jacket. Resumed casting.

The angels who accompany anglers so devised it that the twenty seconds I was engaged in this simple act, both Scholtz and Jimmie were casting and had their heads turned from me and did not see me take off my vivid sweater. Nor was I aware that they had not seen me.

I cast. I felt weeds touch my lure. I reeled in, sitting forward to observe my lure to see if it had caught weeds. I reeled the bright bauble near, drew it alongside, peering down at it.

From below, like a javelin flung vertically up by the devils that inhabit the deep, a muskie rushed.

In a splitting leap, he took my lure from under my face and came like a lightning bolt upward. I flung myself sideways, the muskie slithered against my left shoulder and fell behind me on to the lunch basket. The hooks of my lure entangled in the sweater. With a convulsive leap, the eleven-pounder, all steel bows, flung himself into the air behind my cringing head. And at that very instant, I, recovering my voice, whooped.

Scholtz and Jimmie, just finishing their casts, turned. They beheld, clear, unmistakeable, irrefutable, a handsome muskie in the air above my shoulders, shaking on his fierce snout, my yellow sweater.

"My Goad, man," moaned Scottie, as he watched me recover my senses slowly, and start to fight the impeded muskie.

"Save my sweater," I begged.

"Save the fush," begged Scotty. "It will never be believed. Never in ten thousand years. It's a miracle."

A very brief struggle, and the poor muskie, swaddled in my soaking sweater, was hauled alongside and Scotty lifted it by the gills. And held it, sweater and all, aloft.

And then we saw Scholtz and Jimmie.

They had quit fishing. They had laid their rods in the bows. Their dark guides, Old Noah and Abe, were paddling, crouched and incredulous, towards us. But not so incredulous as their bosses. Scholtz was gripping the sides of the canoe, white and wide eyed. Jimmie was sitting forward, showing his teeth in a brave derisive grin. But there was a mild panic in his face.

"Mon," I heard Scotty behind me, "mon, keep your heid. They think the fish took your sweater off ye. Whush, now."

The two canoes approached, cautiously, and eight eyes stared blankly at the fish, the sweater, Scotty and me.

Scholtz came alongside and put one leg into my canoe to hold us. Jim came alongside and did likewise. The silence was broken only by heavy breathing.

"Gosh," I said, weakly, "did you see that!"

Everybody cleared their throats.

"Gosh," I said, "I reeled alongside to see if I had a weed on. He came straight from below. With that plug all bristling with hooks, he came straight for my face. I was like in a trance. I couldn't move. If he had ever hit me in the face with that plug he'd have torn my face off."

I breathed heavily.

They all cleared their throats.

"Look at the slime on my shoulder," I said, turning to exhibit, in fact, the smear of slime he had left all over my jacket lapel.

"Mon," said Scotty, in a tone full of hidden meaning, "you're in luck today."

"It's the nearest thing I ever had happen," I said,

shakily.

Scholtz was the first.

"How," he said hollowly, "did he get your sweater off?"

"Eh?" I said, looking around as if that little detail had escaped me up to the moment. "Oh, I guess the hooks must have caught. I just felt a swipe, and the sweater went over my head."

"But," said Scholtz, who now had the sodden sweater in his hand to see that it was not torn, "it couldn't."

"What's that?" I asked a little startled.

"I say it couldn't," said Scholtz heatedly. "It simply couldn't take this sleeved sweater off, without removing your jacket."

"Alright," I said, agreeably, "it didn't then."

"But," said Scholtz, "my God, I saw it."

I turned to Scotty and eagerly instructed him to dig the spring scales out of the tackle box and weigh the fish before he let it go. He still had it by the ears, having disentangled the sweater.

I heard Old Noah speak briefly to Abe in Ojibwa. I caught Scotty's eye fleetingly.

"Greg," said Jimmie, with a nice little laugh as between friends, "tell us how it did it?"

"Jim," I said, humbly, "all I know is, I saw the fish coming. I sort of hung in space for a second, unable to move. Then I leaned backwards. It struck me on the chest. I felt a swipe. It was all so instantaneous. Just a kind of swipe, and the next thing I see, is that muskie in the water with my sweater on his snout."

Scholtz looked at Jimmie. Jimmie looked at Scholtz.

"I saw it," said Jim, in a thin voice. "I saw the damn thing rip it right over his head."

"I heard him yell," agreed Scholtz. "And just as I

looked, I saw the fish yank the sweater off him."

"But," said Jim, "it's impossible."

"Yes," said Scholtz. "Take a look at it. The sweater isn't torn or ripped in any way."

"Personally," I said, "I'm going ashore for a rest. Come on, Scotty; chuck the fish in and run me ashore."

"Eleven pounds," sang out Scotty, lowering the muskie into the water and picking up his paddle.

Scholtz and Jimmie followed.

"Mon," said Scotty, quietly, "how are we daein'?"

"We'll have them nuts in a few minutes," I replied.

We all piled ashore. My first concern was my sweater. Scotty and I wrung it out and spread it to dry. Jimmie and Scholtz were engaged in sotto voce conversation down by the canoes. I saw Scholtz slowly and carefully going through the motions of pulling off an imaginary sweater without taking his coat off. Then he shook his head.

I saw Jim eagerly going through the same motions, only swiftly.

"I've seen magicians," said Jim, "take a man's vest off without removing the coat. They did it quickly. Maybe if you do it quickly, it can be done."

"Don't be an ass," cried Scholtz, loudly. "It can't be done, any way."

"If you didn't see it," said Jim, "I'm ready to say I didn't see it."

"But," groaned Scholtz in agony, "I did see it. That's the hell of it. I saw it yank it right off him. And it isn't torn."

"Boys," I called, "why worry? It's over. I might have had those hooks in my cheek and an eleven-pound wildcat tearing the face off me. Let's forget it."

"Forget it?" said Scholtz, coming up the rocks. "He says, forget it."

"Yes, I say forget it," I said, a little heatedly. "I don't claim anything. I don't ask you to believe it. If it is going to ruin our last holiday, I say forget it."

Jim came up and put his hands on my shoulders.

"Listen, Greg," he said earnestly. "The thing is absurd. There is something funny about this. Tell us. How did it do it?"

"Listen, Jim, suppose I tell you it didn't do it?" I demanded coldly.

"But it did," said Jim.

"I say it didn't, so let the matter drop," I said tensely. "Let the whole thing drop."

"Gentlemen," said Scotty, who was eager to be in on this marvel, "I saw it happen right before my eyes. How it happened, the Lord only knows. But I agree with Mr. Clark. I say, let the whole matter drop."

Scholtz glared angrily at us. We glared angrily back. Jimmie laughed uneasily, and it was now four o'clock of an October afternoon and a chill was coming into the air. A loon yelled weirdly in the distance. Old Noah and Abe stood speechlessly below us, leaning on their paddles, their patient old faces full of bewilderment.

"Come on, Scotty," I said quietly.

And in silence we all got back into our canoes and pushed off and continued up the shore for three quarters of an hour, with never another rise from the darkling water, and the wind grew, and the chill; and that creeping dusk of October moved up on us, and suddenly Scholtz called—

"How about the hotel?"

And soon, three canoes were striding across the open for the hotel, rods furled, anglers cuddled down, guides bending and shunting in the short Ojibwa paddle stroke.

Scotty and I went directly to my room for the usual amenities. Jimmie and Scholtz went straight in by the log fire-place and boldly and without preamble stated their case to the half dozen others, mostly Americans (they know about this October fishing); and soon Scotty and I, with our door open, could hear the gales of laughter and the incredulous shouts, and above it all, the insistent, protesting, declaiming voices of Scholtz and Jimmie.

Up the stairs came a stumble of many feet, and all the Americans swarmed in to behold the victim of the miracle. A quiet, unassuming little man, I was; reserved, aloof, in the best British tradition. I had little to say. Nothing to add. It was obvious I did not wish to discuss the matter.

"I'll make an affidavit," shouted Scholtz, "that I saw it."

He was getting more than angry. There was bigotry in his tone.

"Me too," confessed Jim doggedly.

"Come down," said one of the leatheriest of the Americans. "I'm an attorney. I can draw an affidavit. You can get it properly sworn by a Canadian."

Downstairs they all stamped, laughing, damning; and Scotty and I continued the amenities.

And so it came about that I possess two affidavits declaring before God that a maskinonge removed from my person a yellow sweater with sleeves, said sweater being under my coat, and removed without the coat being removed, or the sweater being torn or damaged in any respect.

And on the affidavits being duly sworn and delivered into my keeping, Scotty and I came clean before the assembled brethren in front of the log fire-place.

And the amenities were general.

Principles

Two lovelier brook trout I never saw, and I told Doc so, and thanked him warmly for having me up to his cabin.

They were twins. About 18 inches long, they would go close to two pounds each. They were identical, lying there on the newspaper on the cabin table, with their scarlet and blue jewel spots, their cream and orange fins. Wow!

WOW! I had got them half a mile apart, one on a Jack Sutton red badger streamer, and the other on a tiny little black Williams favorite. I hated to wrap them up. A day like this is like a wedding day or your son's graduation.

"Beauties," said Doc, pleased at my success on his stream.

"Give me a couple more sheets of newspaper." I held out my hand. Doc was wrapping up the garbage over on the cabin sink.

I did the trout up tenderly, folding the paper neatly. I set them over in the corner with my cased rod, creel and gear.

"Here," I said, "let me put that in the incinerator."

"I have no incinerator," replied Doc, rolling up his package tightly. It contained fish entrails, tea leaves, coffee grounds, plate scrapings, crusts and a couple of soup tins. We had been at the cabin only for the afternoon and evening.

"I'll bury it, then," I suggested, reaching for the package. I liked to show my appreciation for the wonderful visit.

"No, no," said Doc. "I just chuck it out the car window along the road."

"Doc!" I said, shocked.

"What?" said Doc.

"You DON'T just chuck it out the car window! Why, my dear man, I've been writing articles for years against that wicked practice. You mean you just heave that garbage out the car window?"

"Oh, I pick a spot, a gully or ravine as we go along," explained Doc, putting the package along with his gear in the other corner. "It isn't on anybody's property. I fling it well back into the bushes."

"But Doc! Suppose everybody . . ."

"Now, look," said Doc. "It lands away back in the brush. The raccoons get it. The crows get it. Mice, birds, ants . . ."

"But the cans, Doc? The paper?"

"The cans rust, the paper disintegrates with the first rain, the leaves fall on it, the vegetation drops on it, it is welcomed back into the soil."

"Well, I don't know." I said, lamely. After all, Doc was my host. It had been a lovely day, a long unforgettable evening. Still, my lifelong principles!

"Garbage is a nuisance around a cabin like this," explained Doc, gently. "If I burn it in an incinerator, maybe the incinerator isn't out when I leave, and the whole place would catch fire. If I bury it, the coons dig it up. So . . ."

We packed up the car, tidied up and closed the cabin. It is a 40-mile drive back to town from Doc's incomparable hideaway. The night was starry, the traffic sparse. We followed our headlights billowing over the back country roads.

"How are you going to cook them?" asked Doc.

"Well, sir," I replied, elbow out the window and very relaxed, "trout of two pounds deserve special consideration. You mustn't just fry 'em, as you would 10-inchers. Indians would cut them in chunks and boil them in heavily-salted water. My wife has a way of grilling them, with bacon."

And for 15 miles, Doc and I discussed with immense satisfaction the various ways of cooking trout, and remembering past feasts over long and happily misspent years.

Doc suddenly braked the car, as we approached a big culvert.

"Here's the place," he said. "Hand me that package. Over in this corner . . . "

I reached in among Doc's gear and found the newspaper package of garbage. I handed it to Doc and he heaved it high and far back into the dense brush of the gully.

"Boiled," said Doc, accelerating. "I like that idea of boiling a big trout."

"The Nipigon guides," I assured him, "always cut up and boil a big trout. And they cup their hands and put a great big double handful of salt in the pot. You've got to have it real briny."

Thus we hummed and rolled the 40 miles homeward, arriving about midnight at my door, where Doc helped me carry my gear in.

My wife had gone to bed. When Doc had left, I hollered up the stairs:

"Come on down here! Come and see the sights!"

In her nightie, she came down, and she knew the way I hugged her that fortune had smiled on me.

With my parcel, I led the way into the kitchen. I turned on the big ceiling light.

"Wait till you see these," I said.

I unwrapped the parcel on the white drainboard.

Tea leaves, coffee grounds, plate scrapings, crusts, two soup tins, fish entrails.

"What on earth's that?" asked my wife in astonishment.

"The collapse of my principles," I said thickly.

The Rugged Outdoorsmen

It was my nephew Pete on the phone.

"Uncle Greg," he said, "how's about coming with us fishing through the ice on Friday?"

"Ice fishing!" I cried, pushing the phone away from my ear. "Are you out of your mind? I gave up ice fishing 30 years ago!"

"Now, look, Uncle Greg," soothed Pete. "It's wonderful. Last weekend we got 11 lake trout, from three pounds to eight pounds."

"Lad," I said, "thank you very much." I shivered in recollection.

"Last weekend," said Pete, "old Mr. McGuire got two five-pounders, and he had hold of one that . . ."

"Who?" I interjected.

"Mr. McGuire," said Pete. "He . . ."

What a dirty trick!

The way you manage the elderly is to quote the exploits of some other old buster who is older than you are. Mr. McGuire is four years older than I am.

I think of him as being 80, 100.

"McGuire?" I said.

"Yes, he had hold of one, through the hole in the ice, that we figured must have been 14 pounds, if not 20."

"Pete," I said, "what was he using for bait?"

"Live minnows," said Pete. "You know, big fat ones. He had a good hold on the monster, and he practically had it through the hole when the damn' line broke . . . "

"Yeah?" I said. "Who else was watching?"

"We were ALL watching," said Pete. "I saw it myself. Its snout. Fourteen, maybe 20 pounds."

I have known McGuire for 40 years. As far as fishing goes, I don't trust him farther than I could kick an anvil.

"Well," I said, "I gave up ice fishing so long ago that I can hardly remember . . . "

"Aw, Uncle Greg," said Pete, "come on! We've got it all organized. You'd have a whale of a time! Don't bother with any tackle."

"Well . . . , " I said. "I'll come along, then."

So I went up into the attic and began organizing for Friday. What a horrible prospect! Ice fishing! There you sit in a little shanty, with a tiny wood stove, and a hole about the size of a suitcase chopped through the ice. In a kind of trance, you dangle your bait or lure down into the shadowy green depths. Half the time you are almost inclined to topple forward and go down into that lovely, serene kingdom.

Outside, the wind not only whistles. It screeches. If you grow weary and push the little hut door open, for a breath of fresh air, you are met with a blast of razor blades. And when it is all over, you have to walk a mile and a half over a lumpy, snow-ridged lake to a camp fire somebody has lit, to show you where the car awaits.

What a fathead! All I had to do was say NO to Pete.

But there was that McGuire.

Eighty, 90,100 years old. And he very near had a 20-pounder . . .

I found my old parka. I don't think I had seen it for 15 years. I found two suits of my old "natural wool" long underwear, a kind of pinky-grey color; itchy but warm. Exploring in the big cotton mattress cover I use for a mothproof bag for all these ancient treasures, I found also a heavy wool stag shirt in big black-and-yellow squares. Thick lumbermen's socks with red tops; horsehide mittens with separate woollen liners.

What a fathead! Ice fishing!

The attic storeroom is unheated, and I gave a premonitory shiver. I tried on the lumbermen's rubbers with leather tops which had lain in a carton for years. I tried on the black-and-yellow stag shirt, and hauled the parka on over it. It was pretty lumpy. But at the thought of old McGuire all bundled up, I felt better. The last time I saw him, in the summer, he looked like a little dried-up old monkey. Ice fishing, for heaven's sake!

From its separate cotton bag, I got out my eiderdown bedroll. It looked withered, but still good. I should take it along, because no doubt we would be staying at night in some leaky old summer hotel rigged up temporarily to accommodate these daffy ice fishermen. I lugged all these souvenirs downstairs—souvenirs of times past, when I had blood in me.

Friday noon, young Pete called me.

"We'll pick you up at 4:30 sharp."

"I'll be ready," I said masculinely.

When the station wagon pulled up in front, I hastily pulled the parka over the stag shirt and came forth. Pete leaped out of the car and took the dunnage bags from me.

"Holy smoke!" he exclaimed.

In the car were old McGuire, in his city overcoat, open to reveal his business suit underneath, and the Matthews boys, Pete's friends, in the back. They were wearing those light quilted ski jackets.

"Well," said old McGuire, as I squashed myself in through the car door, "where are you heading for? Alaska? Or maybe Ungava?"

Pete stowed my bags in the back and away we went.

The station wagon was cozy. Soft music came from the radio. Old McGuire kept talking about the Arctic Circle and Baffin Land, while he peered down at my lumbermen's rubbers. Shortly after clearing the city limits, I took off the parka, with the help of old McGuire. A few miles farther, with the help of the Matthews boys in the back seat, I took off the black-and-yellow stag shirt.

For 40 miles, I watched the night winter landscape passing, while I listened to dramatic accounts of how old McGuire had nearly landed a 20-pounder through the ice last week.

"I have the idea," said McGuire, "it was nearer 30."

"Well, 14 anyway," agreed Pete and the Matthews boys.

Around 7 p.m., we turned into a brilliantly-lighted wayside restaurant for dinner. We had steaks. The waitress, a fine, northern type of young woman, mistook me, on account of my stag shirt, for the guide, I suppose seated at table with my ski-jacketed and city-slicker companions. So she gave me without orders, a fried egg on my steak—an Australian delicacy, I am told, that has found great favor out on the Prairies.

When we got back in the station wagon, old McGuire fell quietly asleep, which was a godsend; and as Pete and the Matthews boys started talking about politics, I fell into a snooze too, and was wakened, around 10 p.m. when we turned off the highway into a well-plowed side road. In 20 minutes, we drew up before a very pretty hotel nestled in the snow, all lights glowing, and on the margin of what I perceived to be a frozen lake.

Young chaps in ski jackets dashed out of the hotel to carry our bags. In a warm, arty lobby we registered; and I was shown into my room. I needed no eiderdown sleeping bag. There was an electric blanket on the bed, already turned on. The pictures on the wall were prints by Mondrian and Picasso. The ski-jacket bellhop was so astonished at my dunnage bags he had to carry in that I paid him $1 for a tip.

I slept like a baby. At 7 a.m., Pete came in and waked me.

"Breakfast at 7:45," he said. "And it's snowing."

"Do we fish out here?" I asked.

"Oh, no," said Pete. "We have to fly about 20 minutes."

In the hall on my way to the washroom (I am pleased to say there was no bathroom attached to my little bedroom) I encountered McGuire. He was wearing a beige-colored outfit, all quilted.

"I never saw pyjamas like those," I remarked.

"This is underwear," said McGuire. "Eiderdown. What's this you've got on?"

He fingered my pinky-grey undershirt.

"That," I said, "is what you call 'natural wool' underwear."

"Oho, yes," said McGuire. "I remember that when I was a kid."

We shaved in silence.

At breakfast, I could hear a plane warming up.

"We're having the Otter," said Pete. "Very cozy."

I went to my room and got into the stag shirt, the parka, the boots, the mitts, and to heck with old McGuire.

In the lobby, the manager saw us off.

"Help yourselves to parkas, gentlemen," he said, indicating a row of parkas hanging on pegs. Old McGuire, who was still in his business suit, with nothing added save a pullover sweater instead of a vest, was assisted into a parka by Pete and the Matthews boys, who were still in their ski jackets. They didn't bother with parkas.

Out we went in the slight blizzard and ran to the Otter awaiting us. It has foam-cushion seats. When its door slammed, it took off on its skis and slid across the frozen lake. I looked out at the wilderness and it was already 500 feet below. Very cozy.

Even in the drifting snow, I could see the little red fishing shacks on the new lake we were circling. When we set down, we taxied to the far end, where we drew up at another smart little hostelry. The pilot pushed the door open. Guides assisted us to alight.

"We'll come in for lunch," explained Pete. "But we'll go right out to the huts now, eh?"

"How far?" I inquired, peering into the light snow. For there were ripples and drifts of snow on the ice.

I heard a roar like an outboard motor and this small object slid into view. It was on skis. It had a small hood, an engine under it. A guide was squatted in it.

"Hop in," said Pete.

I got in behind the guide, and away we scooted over the ice and ripples and drifts, as if we were in a canoe going 20 miles an hour into a head wind. In three minutes, we drew up to a fish hut, painted red. It was bigger than the fish huts I recollected.

"Here we are," said the guide, helping me out of the jigger.

There was no smoke coming from the small chimney.

"No fire?" I questioned, pointing.

"Ah," said the guide, "that's just the ventilator."

He opened the door and I stepped in. It was warm as toast. Instead of a little wood stove, there was a contraption about the size of a football in one corner.

"It's like those little hand-warmers," he explained, "only bigger."

He assisted me off with my parka, my yellow-and-black stag shirt. He sat me down on a foam-cushioned bench and lifted a plywood lid off the hole in the ice. From a plastic bag he carried, he produced a live minnow, and expertly impaled it on a hook which was attached to a reel fastened to the ceiling of the hut.

"You let this down," he said, "until you come to a bit of red wool tied on the line. Then diddle it at that depth until you feel a trout take it, see? Then you feed out line, about 20 feet, until you come to a bit of blue wool tied to the line. Then give a yank! And you've got him."

He reached over by my shoulder and showed me a button in the wall.

"That's the Klaxon," he said. "When you get a

fish, give this button a shove, and some of us will be handy. We'll come and help you get it in."

"I see," I said.

"Do you want a radio, incidentally?" asked the guide.

"A what?" I replied.

The way I said it, he went out and closed the door.

I lowered the minnow until I came to the red wool. I stared down into the lovely, shadowy green depths. Nothing can change that. Not the years. Not the cars. Not the scooters. Nothing. The lovely shadowy green kingdom.

In 30 minutes, I had one trout, a three-pounder. I didn't toot the Klaxon. In another half-hour, I had a better one, on the same minnow, of about five pounds. When I had it up and safe outside on the ice, I reached up and blew the Klaxon.

Out of the quiet drifting snow came a scooter, gliding, jumping.

"Where," I asked the guide, "is old Mr. McGuire's hut?"

"About 400 yards over here," said he. "Want to visit him?"

We scooted across the drifts and ice patches and pulled up at a larger hut than mine.

As I approached the door, I could hear music from within.

"Come in, come in," cried old McGuire, when I pushed it open.

He was in his shirt sleeves.

He had a radio going full blast. He had four trout, two of them three-pounders; one of them a five-pounder like mine; and one at least 10 pounds. He had them hung by the gills from metal pegs on the wall. There were tasselled curtains on the little window.

"Sit down, sit down!" he cried, diddling his line vigorously up and down in the hole in the ice.

"How much does that one go?" I asked, pointing to the maybe 10-pounder.

"Oh, 15," said old McGuire.

"I'd say about 30," I suggested.

He gave me a forgiving look.

"Man," he exulted, "how I love this rugged outdoor life!"

The Book

Mr. Abbott, of the firm of Thorburn and Abbott, new, second-hand and antique booksellers, of Sparks Street, Ottawa regarded me with distaste, and reasonably so. Whenever I appeared in the door of his shop, he tried to conceal his tall frame behind the stacks of new books in the up-to-date main floor of his shop, meanwhile hissing to his clerks to get rid of me, get me out of here! Pssst!

But when I ran him to earth, as I always did, I leeched on to him until he surrendered and escorted me to the locked second floor of his shop, which was the antique and second-hand department—a tremendous storehouse heaped with all his purchases of the libraries of defunct Ottawans. For nearly a century now, Ottawa has been peopled by genteel civil servants who thought it seemly to have libraries, as well as by statesmen, ambassadors and representatives, all of whom were inclined to possess books about Canada. Ottawa has always been a gold mine to lovers of Canadiana.

But I am not a lover of Canadiana. I am narrow. I am choosy, eclectic. All I collect is *piscatoria Canadiana et Americana,* which, being translated, is Canadian and American fishing books. This is why I bored Mr. Abbott. All booksellers dislike one-eyed collectors.

It was a bitter February morning about 9 o'clock that I took Mr. Abbott unawares. He didn't see me until I was in front of him.

"Not a thing up there!" he protested. "I haven't bought anything for two years. Besides, the heat isn't turned on. It's as cold as Greenland up there."

So he put on his hat and overcoat, and up we went to the always-locked second floor. Ah, the lovely dusty heaps—piles, cartons of them! I began pawing them over. Mr. Abbott stood back, sniffing. "You're wasting your time and mine," he muttered.

About the tenth book I picked up, I nearly dropped dead. *Trifles From My Portfolio,* by a Staff Surgeon, Quebec, 1838, Vol. I.

In buying antique books, you have to guard your excitement as if it were your life. I tossed the little book aside carelessly, went on pawing as if nothing had happened.

But what had happened? I had found a treasure every sportsman would give one hind leg for. *Trifles,* in two volumes, printed and published in Quebec in 1838, is by Dr. William Henry. Volume I is all about his experiences in the Peninsular War and the autopsy on Napoleon at St. Helena, which Dr. Henry helped conduct. But Volume II is all about salmon fishing, snipe shooting and the field sports of Canada as experienced by him, an ardent sportsman, in and around Quebec from 1821, when his regiment arrived in Canada from St. Helena, until 1838. The golden days.

Afraid lest Mr. Abbott detect me in my frantic search for Volume II, and keeping my eye on where I had tossed Vol. I, I began to shiver. Mr. Abbott was already shivering and heading for the door. I picked up half a dozen other volumes amid which to hide *Trifles,* Vol. I I handed them to him.

"How much are these?"

He hastily glanced over them. My heart was in my mouth.

"Oh, a dollar apiece," he said, impatiently.

I dropped the others and held *Trifles* behind my back. With my other hand, I extended Mr. Abbott $1. With the sinking heart known to all booksellers, he stared at me.

"What have I done?" he croaked.

I held out *Trifles,* open at the title page.

"Oh, great Scott!" cried Mr. Abbott. *Trifles From My Portfolio!* Where's Volume II?"

"We've got to find it," I said.

"If we do," shouted Mr. Abbott, "it will cost you $24!"

"Done!" I exulted.

We hunted through those thousands of old, dusty books from 9:30 a.m. to winter dark, that day. We looked at every book twice. I missed the appointments with important government people for which I had come to Ottawa. It was in vain.

Eight months later, I got a plain postcard from Mr. Ducharme, of the Librairie Ducharme, over the hardware store on St. Lawrence Boulevard, Montreal:

"I have found one odd copy Volume II of *Trifles,*" it said. "It will cost you $24."

Which proves antique booksellers get together, for revenge.

The Ducharme discovery was the missing mate to

my Ottawa find: for its pages were annotated, in French, in pencil, by the identical hand as in Vol. I.

The little old wanderers are happy together again on my shelf.

Lazy McGriddle

It so happens that to get to Bullhead Bay, where I have had the best big-mouth bass fishing of my life for the past 40 years, I have to pass McGriddle's cottage on its small island fair in the entrance to Bullhead Bay.

Now, Joe McGriddle is without doubt the laziest man I have ever known. He is a lawyer. He smokes a pipe. A big, lardy man, he has this pipe eternally in his teeth, an old, charred pipe, with the tobacco dangling out of it, and fuming. Joe is too lazy even to suck on his pipe. He just lets it burn there in front of his nose.

Oh, I like Joe, all right. Lazy as he may be, he never misses me going into Bullhead Bay. When the signs are right, with a soft south wind and a hint of rain in the air, I have sometimes been up at daybreak and passed Joe's cottage as early as 5 a.m. In fact, I cut my engine well this side of Joe McGriddle's and row past, in order not to wake him or any of the other cottagers around the entrance to Bullhead Bay.

But sure as fate, there is Joe in his nightshirt (he is too lazy to tangle with pyjamas) tottering fatly out to his veranda in the dawn to wave me past.

I figure there haven't been 10 times in the past 40 years that Joe McGriddle has failed to see me go into Bullhead Bay.

And not 10 times that he has not caught me coming out.

"Hi, Greg!" he shouts, waving heartily, as I come steaming in my outboard past his cottage.

And he waves me in.

Well, sometimes I have got only three or four big-mouth bass. But usually I have the six the law allows.

Let me tell you, there is nothing to beat a big-mouth bass. I am sure you have been stuffed full of the fame and glory of the small-mouth black bass. Books have been written about it. Pound for pound, they say, and inch for inch, the small-mouth bass is the gamest fish that swims.

Possibly so. But give me the BIG-mouth bass.

True, he is a coarser, rougher, rowdier cousin of the classically famous small-mouth. But you catch the small-mouth in open clear water, over fine shoals, or in swift rivers; he is an open-water fish. Sure, he jumps and leaps and puts up a terrific fight. But there are no hazards, except the frailty of your tackle. In due time, he tires, and you lift him out with the landing net, reverently. You have mastered a small-mouth bass.

But the BIG-mouth! No clear open water for him! He dwells amid the lily pads in shallow weedy water. Stumps and deadheads are his favorite hiding places. He is a great big rough, tough gourmand who will smash at anything that moves in his jungle territory. Where you have merely to sink a worm or a crawfish or minnow into 10 feet of clear water for a small-mouth, you have to skitter a surface lure, weedless by reason of prongs of wire to part the herbage, to entice a big-mouth to come, like a submarine surfacing, to smash at your lure slithering over the top of lily pads, wild rice, marsh grass, mud rushes.

And when you set the hook, he has a hundred hazards in his favor: ropy stems of water-lily pads, stumps, rocks, bulrushes, unknown hazards hidden in the shallow jungles beyond your ken.

The difference between a small-mouth and a big-mouth is the difference between a nice fancy-dancy boxing match in a high-school gymnasium and a fight in a dark alley down a side street in the meanest part of town.

Well, well, well!

"Hi, Greg!" hails Joe McGriddle, the laziest, inert, fat old pipe-smoking lawyer in my entire acquaintance.

And invariably I haul over and pull up at Joe's dock.

And there is Joe bursting with pride in my catch.

"I bet you," he shouts, "that one will go five pounds!"

Well, if I have three, I give him one.

And if I have six, I give him two; or sometimes three.

He loves bass.

But what can I do? In a way, Bullhead Bay is Joe McGriddle's home territory. His cottage sits right in the entrance to it.

I guess in the past 40 years I must have given Joe 800 bass. That is a modest estimate.

Twenty a year.

Anyway, this last winter, old Dr. Potter, who was the dean, the doyen, seignior, paterfamilins and potentate of our summer colony, passed away.

He was in his eighties. But he owned the smartest speedboat, the fleetest sailing dinghy, the two best canoes (50 pounds each), and the most wonderful collection of fishing tackle, rods, reels, chromium-plated tackle boxes full of 500 lures nobody outside the tackle business ever dreamed of.

For the past 20 years, he did no fishing.

He just bought things, and owned them.

After all, he was 80.

His cottage is fifth along the shore before you get to Joe McGriddle's.

Last week I was up, looking the situation over for the coming season. And when I came past the late Dr. Potter's cottage, there was Mrs. Potter, in her seventies, out planting petunias in the rockeries and looking pretty darned lonely.

So I hove in to her dock and walked up to greet her and squeeze her elbow and tell her how deeply the whole Point would feel her loss and share it with her.

She is a sweet old lady.

"Ah, by the way," I said, with embarrassment proper to the circumstances, "if you are ever thinking of disposing of the dear old Doctor's canoes, or his sailing dinghy, or any of his fishing tackle . . ."

"Oh," said Mrs. Potter, "they're all given away already."

"Dear, dear," said I.

"Yes," she said. "One of Dr. Potter's last requests was I give his boats and his tackle to Mr. McGriddle."

"McGriddle!" said I.

"Yes," said Mrs. Potter, misty in the eyes. "Mr. McGriddle has been the kindest man all these years. The dearest neighbor. Hardly a week went by that he didn't call around at our dock and give us some bass."

"Bass?" said I.

"Yes, he must be a wonderful fisherman," said

Mrs. Potter. "I imagine he must have given us as many as 20 bass a year. Lovely big ones."

"Twenty?" said I.

All I figure is, you can be lazy without being lazy in the head.

A Canoe Of 20 Years

How did I come by this beautiful canoe? Just look at it. One piece of birchbark. And it's 14½ feet long.

You won't see many bark canoes the like of this any more.

How did I get it? Well it was all on account of my not understanding French.

The French I learned at high school gave the word *un*—that's one—a sound like "unh." The sound you make if somebody gives you a slight punch in the belly.

But up in those parts of Quebec where I got this canoe, they say *un* differently. They call it "anh." The sound you make when you accidentally pick up something sticky. Anh!

Now, here's how I got the canoe.

I joined one of those posh Quebec fishing clubs consisting of 60 Americans and 15 Canadians. It had been founded 70 years ago largely by a group of Americans from around Albany and New Amsterdam, and we had something like 200 square miles of lovely lake and stream full of speckled trout.

I bought a handsome new sporting outfit of Harris tweed, including plus-fours, which were in fashion at that time, so as to make a good impression on the older members of the club, many of them wealthy old Americans.

The most attractive feature of this club was the fact that they did not allow anything modern anywhere near it. The only engine was in an old lumberman's pointer in which we were conveyed from the jumping-off place, a tiny hamlet at the end of all roads, to the clubhouse 10 miles up the main lake.

We had nothing but oil lamps. All stoves were wood stoves. Only fly rods were permitted—no bait casting, trolling, spinning.

And every member, on joining, had to buy a birchbark canoe.

No factory-made canoes were permitted.

We had, on the club area, some Indians living, one of whom, the Blue Goose, was the canoe maker. And he got $18 for each canoe.

Oho, they weren't like this one. As I say, you won't see the like of this one any more. There aren't any more big enough birches left in our forests, even our remote forests. So the bark canoes you'll see are made of pieces of bark, stitched together with tamarack root, and then gummed. They are patched together. But not mine. It's one piece. It came off one of the last great birches.

When I arrived for the first time at the hamlet, preparatory to being picked up by the club guardian and portered to the club house, I called, as was the custom, at the guardian's house and paid my respects to Mme. Bernier, the guardian's wife, a fine, stately French-Canadian lady.

After our cup of tea and cheese straws, Mme. Bernier told me, in slow, careful French which she had practised on my American fellow members, that, for *la bonne chance*—for the good luck—it was

139

customary for the members to make a small dona-
tion to the local church, which was in the process of
buying an entirely new set of vestments for the
young priest, himself an ardent trout fisherman
and outdoorsman.

I assured Mme. Bernier that I would be most
happy to contribute, and asked her to suggest how
much I might give.

Now, what she said was *"un dollar."*

But the way she said "anh dollar," I took it to be
"cinq dollars," which is $5.

And inquiring which path to take to the tiny
church, I proceeded, in my Harris plus-fours and
very dashing Tyrolean hat, with brush, to pay my
respects to the young priest and to assure myself of
la bonne chance.

I found him busy sweeping out the church. He
was in an old cassock, green with age and ragged,
and an old peaked cap, and I think he was a little
upset to be caught at such a homely chore and in
such old garments, which he had probably in-
herited with the parish.

However, I did my best to set him at his ease, to
treat him with due reverence, that excessive reverence which we Protestants show young priests,
grave in their youth.

And I concluded our limited conversation by
handing him the five bucks.

M. Bernier, the guardian, now had the pointer
gassed up. But before we took off, he sent for the
Blue Goose, a middle-aged Indian, and I was
solemnly introduced, and I ordered my birchbark
canoe.

It would not be ready, of course, until next year.
In the meantime, I would be loaned one of the ab-
sent member's canoes for this first visit.

I did not know it, but I was already dubbed *"le riche Monsieur Clark."*

News of my magnificent gift to the church had spread.

I had a wonderful 10 days fishing. My guide was the oldest son of Mme. and M. Bernier. He was tireless in his attentions, and took me, I was afterwards told, to some of the secret holes reserved strictly for the president of the club, and old gentleman from Albany worth several millions.

When I was departing, with an iced box with 20 gorgeous trout to take home, the young priest turned out in his best cassock and fine black boots, and his hair slicked back blond and beautiful, along with all the natives of the hamlet, including the Blue Goose.

Munificent gifts are nôt soon forgotten.

It seems the Blue Goose was under some severe penance to the young priest. As far as I was able to gather, from guarded remarks the following year from Mme. Bernier, it had something to do with shenanigans on the part of the Blue Goose with the young ladies of the tribe.

At any rate, the Blue Goose recalled a birch tree he had seen many years before, in a remote and inaccessible region to the northeast of Lac Poisson Blanc, one of our best lakes.

With young Bernier, my guide in the bow, the Blue Goose in the middle as passenger, and the young priest in the stern (with his fly rod projecting aft, though the season was not open) they went to the far end of Lac Poisson Blanc and, with the Blue Goose guiding, they hunted until they found this great birch, this last of the great birches. And they felled it. And with the Blue Goose's ancient art, and at the exact proper season, they stripped off this one beautiful great piece of birchbark, thicker than bull hide, unmarred by through knots, the color of old cordevan leather on the inside, as you see; and tenderly they portaged it and brought it down to Lac Poisson Blanc.

And when I arrived for my second visit to my posh club, here was my canoe. With some of it's pebbly bark, the Blue Goose had even sewn on my initials on the bow: GC.

So, you see, through my misunderstanding of the French tongue, taking "anh" for *cinq*, the Blue Goose's sin is absolved, and I have what they proudly call *"un canot de vingt ans."*

A canoe of 20 years.

It has lasted longer.

The Flat Fifty

Seven years is a long time to plan a fishing trip. To plan, to dream. To study maps and write away to Ottawa for more maps of that far northern region where the speckled trout run to six pounds and the lake trout to 40, and the white man has hardly ever been seen.

Seven lovely winters we had put in, drawing up grub lists, writing to Hudson's Bay Co. factors of remote posts; in imagination packing and repacking our kit bags with the essentials for such a wonderful expedition.

Essentials. I had one essential. The tobacco. The two half-pound plugs of real, old, black, hard Scotch cake for Chief Mukwa, the Cree chieftain who was to meet us and be our guide.

And I let on to nobody else in the party that I had the tobacco. It was to be a gift from one wise woodsman to another. It would make Chief Mukwa my friend, my understanding friend, right from the start.

And here we were at the start. Cooper, Herriot, Milne, Bumpy Lewis and I. We took the train to Sioux Lookout. And there the bush pilot who was to fly us into our secret paradise of trout, leagues and leagues to the far north, met us at the station with a truck to drive us out to the nearby lake where his big plane awaited us.

"I saw Alex yesterday," said the pilot, as he helped me carry my kit bag along the station platform.

"Alex?" I inquired.

"Yes, Mukwa. Alex Mukwa," explained the pilot.

I did not know Chief Mukwa's name was Alex.

"He's expecting you," said the pilot.

Being the oldest of the party, I sat up beside the pilot as we crowded into the plane already jammed with freight for other points north. In a matter of minutes, we had hoicked up and out of Sioux Lookout, and below us spread the vast, stationary wilderness of the true north.

"How old is Chief Mukwa?" I shouted in the pilot's ear,

"Alex? Oh, he's around thirty-five."

It was too hard to converse, so I contented myself with planning our meeting with Chief Mukwa. I had the tobacco, the two precious plugs, on the top of my kit bag so I could get them out immediately on landing and make my presentation.

For in all the old books, in the Hudson's Bay Co. stories and in W. J. Tyrrell's *Across the Subarctics of Canada,* I had read of the ceremonial nature of tobacco, and how the Indians of the great brigades used to spell off every hour for a smoke of their black stick tobacco. And how, on meeting strange Indians, it was important to make a presentation of tobacco immediately on meeting.

Believe me, it was no easy task to get this tobacco. Indeed, having had seven years to plan our trip, I had used about six of them locating a tobacconist in Victoria who imported this black cake from Scotland. And I had found great satisfaction in obtaining two half-pound plugs at $1.10 each.

And they were ready, in the top of my kit bag.

Do everything right, is my motto.

"Alex meets you," shouted the pilot, "at a portage into his lake. I can't let down in his lake. Too narrow. Too many rocks."

"Good," I shouted.

"Only a short walk across," yelled the pilot, "from where I let you out. Alex will have a couple more Indians to carry your stuff over."

"We can carry our stuff," I asserted clearly.

And glanced back at Cooper, Herriot, Bumpy and Milne, huddled on the baggage in their bush clothes. They were playing gin rummy.

So I devoted myself to doing the looking for us all. I stared out the window at the strange, stationary landscape, the lakes, the ponds, the spruce, the muskegs. And of course, never a sign of Man.

And in less time than you can imagine, the pilot yelled:

"We land on the big lake, see? And that's Alex's lake just beyond it."

We banked, throttled down, took the long coasting in, bumped, and taxied to a sand beach where we could see three Indians standing.

"The tall fellow," said the pilot, "is Alex."

We touched the pontoons on the beach. The Indians waded out and hauled us snug. Out the doors we crawled.

"Chief Mukwa?" I said, warmly, holding out my hand.

"That's me," said the tall man, with a wide smile.

We humped the baggage and the rod cases and the tackle bags ashore. I hastily got my two plugs of the ancient, veritable Scotch cake out of the top of my kit bag. Seizing a moment when Chief Mukwa was free of luggage, I signalled him aside.

"Chief," I said, "I have brought you a small gift of tobacco."

Chief Mukwa accepted them gravely, examined them closely, sniffed them, tried to dent one of them with his thumb nail.

"Thank you," he said.

And put them in his side pants pocket.

We got the plane pushed free, with shouted agreements to be picked up right here five days hence, ceiling permitting.

We proceeded to distribute the luggage for portaging. Chief Mukwa and his two sturdy tribesmen took most of it. We sports took our rod cases and tackle bags.

Over the portage we went in three minutes.

Chief Mukwa had a beautiful big square-stern canoe awaiting us, and two smaller ones. On the big canoe was a handsome big 30-h.p. outboard engine, brand new. On the smaller canoes, five-horse engines.

Quickly we were stowed. Engines popping and roaring, we were away across Chief Mukwa's lake, the one that has been the traditional trapline of Chief Mukwa's family for countless generations, here in the remote and ancient hinterland of

Canada.

We landed at Chief Mukwa's camp. He had three cabins and two large tents. His wife and her two sisters, in slacks and sport shirts, greeted us and showed us to our cabin.

It had a radio in it, on.

The walls were decorated with autographed photos of Marilyn Monroe, Gregory Peck and other celebrities.

Chief Mukwa called us to lunch almost before we had got our gear unpacked.

We had jellied tongue, salad, grilled trout, canned peaches.

Then we went fishing, in the smart outboard canoes. The fishing was terrific. In lake, pond, stream, with little portages, we fished the five days, ate like kings, slept on spring mattresses, were waited on hand and foot.

As we were preparing to leave, the last noon, Chief Mukwa brought me a gift.

A flat fifty of cigarettes, cork-tipped.

"You might be running short," he explained, kindly. "I got lots of them. I fly everything in, you know."

The Trophy

"Say," said my neighbor Greene—my summer neighbor, that is—"you know that muskie head you gave the boys?"

"I sure do," I said proudly.

"Well, it smells," said Greene, regretfully.

The Greene boys had asked me, as a fisherman

of wide repute, if I ever got a really big pike or other namely fish, would I save the head for them. They are Boy Scouts. And it seems Boy Scouts are on the hunt for wolf heads, tiger heads, alligator heads, or any other large and savage heads. And they dry them and mount them on wooden shields, like trophies.

Being a fisherman of wide repute, my wife caught this 44-pound muskie, as they call the muskellunge. A member of the pike family, it grows to immense size in the Great Lakes, St. Lawrence and Mississippi water-sheds. It has a face like a scoop shovel, with fangs two inches long, and dreadful baleful eyes like a werewolf. The one my wife caught I hit with an iron poker that happened to be in the boat at the moment, thus subduing it so that two neighbors in canoes could come and help me tow it ashore.

My own preference, as far as eating is concerned, is for small fish. I suppose my favorite of all fish is the whitebait, to be had only in the British Isles. It is a tiny fish that, when fried, is about the size of a match. And a hot vegetable dish full of about 300 whitebait is my idea of fish at their best. Next come sardines. With a tin of sardines, a purple onion, two slices of fresh bread face to face with thick cold butter, I am prepared to head for Alaska, the next war, or a muskie-fishing trip.

So it was that I was not prepared to eat the 44-pound muskie my wife caught. On the pretext of giving the head to the sons of the Greenes, I gave them the whole fish, thus getting out of the difficulty of interring it.

Since the Greene boys wanted to show it around the neighborhood, it was a little past the edible stage by the time they cut its head off. Greene Père had to bury it. It was quite a task.

"But THANK you," said Greene, "very MUCH!"

I conferred with the boys on the matter of curing the head, which alone, a mere skull, weighed five pounds.

"You hang it," I propounded, "in a tree, safe from raccoons or other marauders. And the flies, ants, bugs, beetles and other creatures will chew off all the flesh, leaving only the ghastly head. By the time summer is over, it will be ready to varnish and tack by its gill covers on to a wooden shield.

"That's the way the Scoutmaster told us," they agreed.

"But be sure," I warned, "to prop the mouth open, wide—wide as it will go. So that when it is dried, it will be gaping at you, ferociously, its white fangs gleaming, and its empty eye sockets glaring."

That is the way they hung it. And it was a masterpiece. It was so dried, by summer's end, that they could take the stick out that propped its jaws agape. They brought it home in a carton all by itself, in the back of the car. And hung it down in the cellar.

It was Mrs. Greene who first noticed the aroma.

"That thing," she said, to all her males, "smells."

The boys went down and smelled it, and said they couldn't smell a thing.

"I wish," said Mrs. Greene, "the Clarks would eat their own fish!"

But the past few humid days, there could be no more doubt.

"I'm sorry," said Greene to me. "But it smells. What do you suggest?"

"Why," I said, "put it outside somewhere. Hang it out in the garage or somewhere. A little more time and you won't smell it at all."

Greene went home and moved it from the cellar to the garage.

What a fearsome sight it was! It looked far more ghastly in October than it did in August. It had withered to a brown the color of old glue. The snarl on the wide-open jaws was monstrous. Its eye sockets seemed emptier, its fangs longer, fiercer, whiter.

But since Greene could not find any nail, hook or other support on which to hang it, he just laid it on top of a box in the garage.

And went to bed.

It was supper time next day, Tuesday, that Greene telephoned me.

"You know that muskie head?" he asked.

"I sure do," I said proudly.

"Well, it's gone!" said Greene. "The boys got home from school and went to look at it where I left it in the garage. And it was gone."

"Put an ad in the papers," I suggested. "In the Lost and Found . . ."

"I'll THINK about it," said Greene.

It was 6:40 a.m. next day, Wednesday, that Greene called me next.

"You know that muskie head?" he said.

"Do you know what time it is?" I countered.

"Well, it's been found," he said. "And you'd better get over here as fast as you can before the lawyers arrive."

"Lawyers!" said I, hanging up and hastily pulling on my pants.

I discovered, on arriving at the Greenes', that the Misses Binnie, two highly-respected maiden ladies of the neighborhood, have a tomcat named Trixie. He weighs about 12 pounds, and has the habit of staying out all night.

149

Trixie is a soiled-grey-colored cat, somewhat scarred from many a midnight battle, but large and strong of limb.

The elder Miss Binnie rises at 6 o'clock in the morning and goes to the back door to pick up the two quarts of milk.

In so doing, she peeps out past the door, in her dressing gown, and softly calls:

"Kitty, kitty, kitty!" in case Trixie is home from his devotions.

Well, this morning, she called kitty.

And from the shrubbery at the bottom of her garden there appeared as ghastly a monster as ever St. George slew.

Sliding along the ground toward Miss Binnie came a dreadful brown, mummy-colored horror, its enormous jaws agape, its teeth bared in a horrific snarl, its empty eye sockets flashing with fire.

Trixie, having stolen the muskie head from the Greenes the night before and hidden it, was determined to get his prize home. And in his manoeuvres to get a grip on it and to avoid the fangs, he had got his head stuck in the rear of the head.

By all appearances, he had had a pretty tough night trying to rid himself of the head and climb fences. He was in a lather when, on hearing his beloved mistress calling him, "Kitty, kitty," he slid along the ground, shoving the head in front of him, willy nilly.

It was at this juncture that the elder Miss Binnie fainted, throwing the milk bottle in the air in so doing.

The crash of the milk bottle brought the younger Miss Binnie. By this time, Trixie was half-way across the yard, heading for home.

It was the younger Miss Binnie's screeches that

wakened the neighborhood and all the Greenes.

No lawyers had arrived by the time I got there.

The Misses Binnie were in the tender care of the ladies round about.

In order to get Trixie out of the muskie head, Greene and the other male neighbors had to stand on the muskie's snout, ruining it for ornamental purposes.

So it came to a sad end, in a garbage can, with lid on.

"But NEXT year!" I promised the Greene boys.

"Mmmm-hmmmmm?" said Greene.

Not Even Mister Wilson

Well, sir, it is generally conceded among my newspaper colleagues that I can smell a good fish restaurant at a distance of three blocks. I don't claim this, I think TWO blocks would be fairer.

All men have their private embarrassments. The thing that has haunted me all my life is that I could never decide whether I liked catching fish more than I liked eating them. This is a shameful thing. If you read the literature of angling, which consists of more than 60,000 volumes, you will realize that eating fish is a mere side issue.

Not for me, I think fish are concerned with the survival of the human race. Now, you take steaks. I think steaks are the most over-rated of all human provender. All steaks taste the same. But fish! No two fish taste the same. I don't mean merely species, say, speckled trout or haddock. I mean in the infinite variety of the ways of cooking them.

I can still remember my young, radiant father, Joe, catching two smallmouth black bass on a rocky shore. He skinned 'em. He filletted them. Into a frying pan, with butter, he put them with reverence on the little bonfire I had been entrusted with. I was eight.

Maybe that was the beginning of my dedication.

Thus, whenever we newspapermen swarmed together on the scene of some great disaster, or some stately event like the founding of the United Nations in San Fancisco, we, being on expense accounts and staying at the best hotels (out of respect for the prestige of our employers), would file our dispatches with the telegraph offices, and then somebody would cry:

"Where do we eat?"

Whereupon I would step forward and deliver my eulogy.

First, I would remind the boys of the debt mankind owes to the finny nation. I would describe ancient man, that skinny hairless ape cowering in his cave amid a world dominated by sabre-toothed tiger, hairy mammoths and other monsters. Subsisting on berries and nuts in season, and venturing out, when the coast was clear, to the nearby river to catch a mess of fish. As proof of this, I pointed out that all the great centres of civilization were located on rivers, or the sea. On the spiritual level, I would mention that Jesus and His friends were fishermen, and gave us the great message. Then, changing pace, I would mention sole à la Scott, grilled finnan haddie with scalloped potatoes, *truite au bleu*. Then I would bring in oyster, or clams, followed by lobster thermidor. When I saw I had them drooling, I would refer to bouillabaisse, obtainable at certain restaurants, if they would follow me.

How, I would demand did ancient man get out of the caves and come forth to conquer the world? He got out of them by eating fish.

By then I had them in the cup of my hand. And they followed me.

In this fashion, I came to know many, if not most, of the great fish restaurants of the Western world. Of course, we being on expense accounts, and stopping at the best hotels, there was always a good fish restaurant within two or three blocks. There always is. All this stuff about me being able to smell out a great fish restaurant within three blocks is sheer nonsense. I do not smell them out. I am not a fish beagle. I just ask the first cop.

But I admit I have known all the great fish restaurants of our time. Mostly, they come and they go. Few survive three generations. What happens is that the old genius of the place grows older and hands the business over to his son; or to his daughter and her husband. The magic goes out. Or worse, a bunch of tycoons and business executives come into the act. It is a fact that the great fish restaurants have, among their firmest patrons, the tycoons and executives of big business.

The reason for this is obvious. Tycoons don't eat steak. Who would want to add to his metabolism the flesh of the stupidest animal in our collection, a bug-eyed steer which spends most of its life lying down? No, sir! Fish. They are brilliant, dwelling in a swift and perilous element, whether river or sea. There is beauty in them living. There is beauty in them on your plate, with quaters of lemon.

Now, these damn tycoons, who in time become on first-name acquaintance with the old restaurateur, take him to lunch at THEIR club. And they persuade him to incorporate. They not only offer him a big gob of money, maybe $100,000, but assure him of a life-time job managing the new establishment.

He does not know that these tycoons are more interested in making money than in cooking fish. In a few months, the poor old man retires, disgusted; and in a couple of years, the tycoons have to start looking for a new fish restaurant. But in the meantime they have got their capital back out of the reputation of the old man.

However, some survive. And you will find one or two in London, Boston, Paris, San Francisco, Washington. For example, in London, Scott's. I found Scott's on Sept. 3, 1916, during World War I, a lovely misty London evening, I remember it well.

It is not easy to get into Scott's, like most great fish restaurants. It consists of three levels: a main-floor dining room, where London business executives entertain each other; an upstairs level, where elderly business executives entertain their nieces to luncheon or dinner, and, best of all, a basement level, which you can get at in two fashions—either down a broad staircase, as you come in the front entrance, or via a sort of special entrance through the tap room, which is on the side street, named Great Windmill Street.

The uniformed doorman, noting my Canadian badges on my first attempting to enter by the front door on Coventry Street (which is just 43 paces due east of Piccadilly Circus), informed me that he had a nephew in Saskatchewan, and wondered if I knew him, name of Jenkins.

When I regretted that I did not, he said that there was quite a line-up ahead of me. But if I would just pop around the corner, on to Great Windmill there, I should find a stairway down into the tap room.

"Once in there, make yourself at home," he said. "The head waiter of the lower level will pop in from time to time and take note of you. That's the quickest."

I popped around the corner and found the staircase to the taproom. There was a bar, with about 10 stools on which sat large-bottomed Englishmen in conversation with the two elderly white-coated barmen. Behind the bar, shoulder high, were five or six huge casks containing the varieties of sherry and port. On the other side of the little tap room were cubicles, each capable of accommodating six people. I found an empty one, though hats, coats and umbrellas were hanging on the pegs of the cubicle walls.

I was about to withdraw when one of the elderly barmen called to me:

"Hang up! I'll be with you in a mo."

So I hung up my trench coat and cap and stick on a free hook and sat me down. The barman brought me a mild and bitter in a metal mug.

In a few moments, a head waiter in black jacket and striped trousers came in from a door beside the bar. He beckoned to two of the fat-bottomed gentlemen on the stools, and glanced at me with raised eyebrows. I nodded. The gentlemen followed him.

By the time I had sipped through my pint of mild and bitter, and several other Englishmen had come in and taken places in the cubicles and on the stools, the head waiter returned, smiled at them, and then gave me the signal. I followed him, and was shown to a table in the crowded basement level.

It was fabulous. The waiters were old, slow and kindly. The customers were all so intent on their

food that they never looked up at a bashful new-
comer arriving in their privileged midst. I can
remember what I had, on that misty London evening 50 years ago, as if it were yesterday. It was
lobster bisque soup; a half portion of whitebait; sole
à la Scott. And to finish, two scoops out of the blue
middle of a prime Stilton cheese.

"Coffee?" asked the old waiter, who had guided
me through this wonderful meal.

"Tea," I said.

"Good for you, sir!" said he. "With no milk or
sugar?"

"Right!" said I.

Well, I've been back many and many a time
since—in that war, and the Vimy Pilgrimage; the
abdication, the coronation, the Papal coronation
(on which I came home via London, for you know
what!) World War II; and so on and so on. Of
course, I was not entirely faithful. I did not fail to
visit Rule's and Madame Prunier's, down St. James's Street, and Wheeler's, whose proprietor,
Bernard Walsh, was as interested in coursing
greyhounds here in the snowshoe-hare swamps of
Canada. And we had much to talk about besides
oysters and fish.

It was Christmas of 1964 I made my last visit to
Scott's. I came in by the side door, the Great Windmill side. The barmen did not recognize me, and I
didn't recognize them. I hung up my duds and
stick. The head waiter came in. He did not recognize me. I did not recognize him. We were even. He
lifted his eyebrows. I nodded. And in due time, he
escorted me through into the crowded old familiar
basement level.

He showed me to my table.

"Would you care for a cigar, sir?" he asked, bowing.

"Cigar?" I said, astonished.

Why, I had barely sat down.

"I'm sorry sir," said the head waiter. "But pipes are not permitted in the restaurant."

"Oh," I exclaimed, snatching my pipe from my teeth and putting it in the glass ash tray. "I'm sorry!"

"Not at all, sir," said the head waiter, bowing and moving off.

I glanced about. The English diners were, as usual, minding their food. Not one appeared to have noticed my little misadventure.

When my waiter, an old one, arrived, I studied him. He did not recognize me, I did not recognize him.

"What," I asked, tapping my pipe in the ash tray, "is this business about pipes?"

"Oh, no, sir," said the old man. "Pipes are not permitted in the better-class restaurants in London."

So he went into the menu. For old time's sake, I decided to recover, if I could, the menu I chose in 1916, a long time ago.

With one deviation. A half dozen of "the best"' that is, the chubby little Whitstable natives, oysters beyond belief.

We agreed on the lobster bisque, the soup; we agreed on a half-portion of whitebait. These are tiny fish, about the size of a wooden kitchen match, which they cook, apparently, in deep fat like French fries; and they come in a hot bowl, and you eat the little things, as you might potato chips. The English are wonderful. They never look. You can eat them with a fork, if you dare. But I like to eat them with my fingers. Then we had sole à la Scott, and the Stilton was as blue as ever. And the biscuits as crisp and dry.

"Would you," I asked my old waiter, who hovered around, "ask the head waiter to speak to me."

In a moment, the head waiter was before me, a fine-looking man with a great crest of tough grey hair.

"Sir?" he asked.

"Now, about this pipe business," I began.

"I'm dreadfully sorry," said he, "if I embarrassed you."

"No, no," I assured him. "But what occurs to me is this. Suppose the Prime Minister of the United Kingdom, Mr. Wilson, were to appear here?"

The head waiter regarded me blankly.

"He never," I said, "is without his pipe in his teeth, or in his hand."

The head waiter stared at me with a growing expression of horror.

"Good heavens!" he said, and, with a bit of a bow, vanished.

My old waiter returned with my tea: no milk, no sugar.

In a couple of minutes, the head waiter returned.

He had obviously been in conference.

"Sir," he said, "with regard to your pipe . . . "

"Please don't bother," I said, tapping out its cold ashes and putting it in my pocket.

"You mentioned," said the head waiter, "if the Prime Minister, Mr. Wilson, were to come in?"

"I did." I agreed.

"We will make no exceptions," said the head waiter.

We shook hands.

That is what I mean about the great fish restaurants.

They are run by men of principle.

Salmon

Every man to his taste. When I found myself in Scotland, with a free day ahead of me, and the village I was in just half-way between the River Dee and the River Don, there came the one thought into my mind: salmon!

Scottish salmon! Caught on the salmon fly:

It was not easy to sell the idea to my companion, who was Louis Jaques, the distiguished photographer of *Weekend Magazine.*

"Look at the weather!" cried Louis. The Scottish mist was beating on the window panes with a loud sound not unlike Canadian rain.

"Perfect for fishing," I mentioned.

"Lousy for photography," said Louis.

"Well, if you prefer to lie around the hotel," I suggested, "I'll get Robert, the proprietress's son, to come with me . . ."

"Aw, I'll come and chauffeur you," growled Louis.

We had a little rented car. Robert came with us, because he had all the slamon tackle, and was an ardent salmon fisher who jumped at the chance for a day on the river.

We chose the Don. It is a smaller river than the Dee, and perhaps not so well known, but still a very famous Scottish salmon river. We drove over the high, rain-swept moors to the tiny village of Glenkindie and called at the Glenkindie Arms, an inn as tiny and sweet as the village of five houses around it. There we were directed to the house of the laird, Captain Leith, who is a son of Lord Burgh. The captain being out on the moors with his guns, Mrs. Leith gave us immediate permission to fish any part of the Don they owned, which was six miles of it.

I think Louis would have liked to have gone in and sat chatting with Mrs. Leith while we went to the river, for she was a fine young lady in tartan trews, and very comely.

But instead he drove us to the river; and Robert and I, dressed in high waders to our waists, and wearing thick woollen sweaters, rigged our salmon rods, mounted the fly called the Torrish, and went joyously to work.

The pools of the Don are magnificent; not large and raging, but quick, leaping and gay. It rained all day. We fished two miles. We never got a rise or a boil or a touch. We saw neither hide nor hair of a fish. But we had a wonderful day. About every hour on the hour, Louis Jaques in the little car would come and hail us from afar, inquiring fiercely, in his new-learned Scottish idiom, if we were daft. At 7 p.m. we allowed him to pick us up in the car at a bridge and drive us back to Glenkindie Arms, where dry clothes awaited us.

We asked if we might have a bite to eat, and were ushered into the small dining room.

What do you suppose was on the plates set before us, on lettuce?

Aye, salmon!

"Hooray!" I shouted. "To think we came 3,000 miles to fish all day and never got a strike, and then have salmon for our supper!"

Louis Jaques leaned down and inspected the salmon on the lettuce narrowly.

160

"It's tinned," he hissed.

"Canned salmon?" I faltered.

"Aye, tinned," corrected Robert.

Louis sat back with a wild surmise.

"What do you bet," he gloated, "it's Canadian salmon? Canadian sockeye?"

The whole day began to take on a beautiful grotesque possibility. Louis asked the waitress to bring us the tin from which the salmon came. She brought it. Louis studied the label with an expression of growing consternation on his face.

"Socra Salmon," he read, in a ringing voice. "Product of Kamchatka, U.S.S.R.!"

When you go fishing, you sometimes catch the damndest things.

Anyway, Louis laughed all the way home across the moors.

Well Met

The bus was fairly full when I boarded it, down around City Hall. In these New York buses, I like to get a seat as close as possible to the rear exit. Especially now, with this fishing rod in my hands.

It was a two-piece fly rod I had bought for Gil Purcell in one of the numerous tackle shops in the City Hall area. The tube in which the rod was encased was five feet long. Pretty awkward, by the time I would get uptown.

The seat immediately in rear of the back exit was occupied, but the one behind it had room for me. The slender grey-haired gentleman squeezed over to the window to make room for me.

"Ah!" he said, affably. "A fishing rod, if I'm not mistaken!"

"You're right," I replied, setting the tube upright between my knees.

"A fly rod?" he asked.

"Right again!" I said, happy to be sitting beside so knowledgeable a man in this tempestuous, ignorant city. "Are you a fly fisherman?"

"Of sorts," he said. "I like fishing in all its forms."

I turned to look at him. Sixty maybe, quietly dressed, with a thoughtful face. He made me think of a university professor.

"Actually," I said, "this is a rod I've bought for a friend back in Canada. I'm supposed by my friends to be something of an authority on rods, and this involves a certain amount of shopping, which I love."

"Ah, you're a Canadian?" said he. "Just on a visit?"

"Three or four days," I said. "We're allowed to bring home $100 worth of goods every four months. And I regret to say most of mine is in fishing tackle."

"It's an expensive hobby," said my seat mate.

"Are you a New Yorker?" I inquired.

"No, no," he said, "I'm a visitor too. Just here for a couple of weeks. I'm in finance. And my work keeps me moving about the country most of the time. But I manage to get in a little fishing."

"Where do you do most of it?" I asked.

"I have no particular favorite," said he, "due to the nature of my work. I've fished a good deal in the South. Bass in Florida. Sea fishing, of course, in Florida and California."

"Ah!" I said, warming.

"Yes," he said, sensing my interest. "But I think

162

of all the fishing I've had, I like fly fishing the best. My work takes me into many of the resort areas—the Adirondacks, Wyoming, Maine, the Pacific states for steelhead, wherever there are fashionable hotels and that sort of thing. In the financial business, you have to go where finance is. And it is astonishing how much of it there is around fishing districts."

We laughed. The bus was filling up.

"Where do you get off?" he asked.

"Forty-second," I said, mentioning my hotel. "Have you ever fished in Canada?"

"No," he said, "but I have been thinking of it lately. There must be a lot money in Canada nowadays."

"I wasn't thinking of money," I remarked, reaching for my wallet in my breast pocket. "But if it is fish you are interested in, I'd like to show you a few snapshots . . ."

From my wallet I took the one of my wife with her 44-pound muskie.

"Good heavens!" said my seat mate, studying it. "A monster!"

"Here's some bass." I handed him another. "That large one is 5½ pounds. The others are all over three."

"On the fly?" asked my knowledgeable friend.

"No, bait casting," I admitted. "But look at this color print."

I handed him my prize.

"Kamloops trout," I said, "Caught at the mouth of the Adams River in the Shuswap Lakes."

He studied the snapshot with an intake of breath.

"Six and half," I said, "that one on the left. Then 5½, that one caught by my wife on a 4½-ounce rod."

163

"Fly?" checked he.

"Yes, SIR!" I said. "And next to it, a 4½. Ah, if you ever come to Canada, you head for the Rocky Mountains."

"Beautiful!" he said, reluctant to let the snapshot go. "Have you any more?"

I shuffled through my wallet.

"I'm sorry I haven't got some of my New-foundland salmon pictures," I regretted. "Or some of my northern Quebec. If you want to see a beautiful thing, it is a four-pound male eastern brook trout, in his full glory."

He handed me back my snapshot of the Adams River.

"We're at Thirty-sixth," he mentioned.

"Oh!" I said, stuffing my wallet back in my pocket, and taking a grip on the rod case.

For the bus was now packed to suffocation.

"I'd better start now," I suggested, as two large ladies pushed their posteriors against my shoulder.

"I'll help you off," said my friend, quietly. "When we get to Forty-second, you push through and I'll hand you your rod case."

"Good," said I.

We came to Forty-second.

I was up. I leaned down and shook hands with my friend, warmly. He patted my shoulder, I shoved past the large ladies and several small ones and five or six assorted men. When I got on the step, my friend pointed the rod case to me, and I seized it and waved goodbye.

"Thank YOU!" I called, in the New York air.

On the way to the hotel, I dropped into a cigar store for some tobacco. I reached for my wallet.

It was gone.

GONE!

With $45—two twenties and a five!

I hastily retraced my steps along the swarming street. But I realized it was hopeless.

The doorman at the hotel told me to telephone the bus terminal lost-and-found. But you could see he had not much faith in the possibilities.

I told my wife.

I told the room clerk. And the elevator man. Nobody was much interested.

At 5 p.m., the room clerk hailed me.

"A parcel for you," said he, handing me a manila envelope.

In it was my wallet. With a note.

Dear Mr. Clark:

I am keeping the $45 and also the color print of the Adams River Kamloops. I must say I was in expectation of more than $45. But the color print will make a good conversation piece in my future financial operations. Tight lines!

Yours for good fishing,
THE FINANCIER.

The Fish That Flew

Herriot at the wheel, the two of us were speeding north at 5 o'clock in the morning. Except for an occasional scurrying truck heading cityward, the highway was beautifully deserted.

"It will be a joke on us," I said, relaxing, "if we get there too late."

"We won't be too late," assured Herriot, with some of last night's excitement still on him.

"Well, O.K.," I said. "Tell me again, as unemotionally as you can, why you phoned me last night."

"Here it is," said Herriot, taking a deep, appreciative breath. "As I told you, I was driving down from North Bay. About 6 o'clock, p.m., I come to this young fellow hitch-hiking. He didn't have any baggage. He had on blue jeans and an ordinary red and black stag shirt. So I figured he was a local boy that I could give a lift to, a couple of concessions."

"The last time I had impetigo," I said, "and the two last times I had fleas, was from picking up strangers on the road."

"Anyway," said Herriot, "when he got in, he said he was just going down the highway a couple of concessions. So I asked him where he worked."

Herriot paused and took another deep joyous breath of recollection.

"He told me he worked at the Pancake Pond Trout Hatchery!"

"Go on," I urged.

"I then suddenly realized we had just passed the sand road," went on Herriot, "leading in to the Pancake Pond Trout Hatchery. I then asked him how everything was going at the hatchery."

Herriot shifted his seat and took a more masterful grip on the steering wheel.

"Aw, go ON!" I protested.

"When he told me," said Herriot, "I nearly went into the ditch!" "We're cleaning out," he says, "the north pond with all the adult breeding speckled trout in it."

"What are you doing with them?" I asked.

" 'They're being shipped,' " says he, " 'tomorrow.' "

"TOMORROW! That's today! They are being shipped in special big oxygenated tank trucks to be

planted in public waters for the sportsmen to
CATCH!"

"Did he mention," I asked, "where they are being
planted?"

"No, no!" said Herriot. "I didn't want to arouse
his suspicions by being too curious, for fear he
would clam up. All I asked was WHY they were
cleaning out the adult breeding trout; and he said
the hatchery was getting a fresh strain of trout
from northern Quebec, for breeders. They've had
these breeders now for six or seven years, and want
a fresh strain."

"Did he say how big they are?" I asked.

Playing a tune with his fingers on the steering
wheel, Herriot said lyrically:

"One and a half to four pounds! And 1,500 of
them!"

"Holy," said I, "doodle!"

"Now, our problem is this," said Herriot. "The
boy told me three of these big oxygenated tank
trucks are coming. Naturally, they won't all go to
the same place. They won't, all three of them,
dump all those fish in one place."

"Naturally," I agreed.

"So what we've got to do," explained Herriot, "is
pull off the highway a hundred yards or so from
where that sand road runs in to the hatchery. We
can have the hood of the car up, as if we were having engine trouble. Naturally, the hatchery people
wouldn't want anybody FOLLOWING them."

"Right," said I.

"Therefore," said Herriot, strategically, "it is our
job to pick which of the three trucks we will follow.
Do you follow me?"

"I'd say the THIRD one," said I.

"Exactly," agreed Herriot. "If we followed the

167

first or the second, the one following might spot us snooping."

"Snooping," I reflected. "Do you think it is fair of us to follow that truck?"

"Look," said Herriot, "all's fair in love, war and fishing. All the local people around the hatchery will know where they're gone. All the locals wherever they are dumped will know. What's the matter with a few of us city people being in on the deal?"

"O.K.," I submitted. "But I want you to know I don't care much about eating these hatchery trout. They taste of hog's liver and peanuts, or whatever it is they feed them in the ponds."

"At least," gloated Herriot, "we'll have the fun of having maybe a four-pound trout on a three-ounce fly rod!"

"Of course," I subsided, trying to recapture in my mind the indescribable sensation of a big trout rising to the fly; the slight dip of the rod tip as the trout boils; the strike; and then the sensual feel of the fragile rod throbbing.

"My guess," said Herriot, "is, they'll plant the trout in streams, so they can distribute themselves up and down. They don't like to dump trout all in one place in a lake."

"Let it be streams," I said devoutly.

For we had brought our hip-length rubber boots, in addition to all our rods, flies, landing nets, gear.

In less than two hours, we were at the sand road leading into Pancake Pond Trout Hatchery.

At 7:25 a.m., parked with our hood up a couple of hundred yards short of the entrance, we had the glorious satisfaction of seeing a procession of three large yellow tank trucks come from the north and turn into the road. We could even see the rigging of the oxygen tanks set at intervals along the series of smaller tanks of which the outfits consisted.

"Do you think they spotted us?" I asked.

"Not a chance," said Herriot.

"How long will they be?" I queried.

"Not very long," said Herriot. "You don't waste any time handling adult trout. They've probably got the pond lowered already, and all they do is bail the trout out into the aerated tanks with big dip nets."

What a spectacle! What a pity that we were here, like hi-jackers, lying in wait!

I went around to the trunk, opened it, and checked to see nothing was missing—rods, reels, waders, flies, landing nets.

An hour went by. Two hours. Traffic was now full belt up and down the highway. A couple of passenger cars came out the sand road, paying us no attention.

Then we heard the growls.

"Here comes ONE!" said Herriot, lowering the hood and signalling me aboard.

But it was not one. It was all three, one right behind the other in the clouds of dust of the road.

They turned north.

At a hot clip, they went into high, one behind the other.

We had to hustle to keep them in sight.

Less than 12 miles up the highway, we had to slacken speed on the third truck. They were turning in on a road to the right.

"What . . . ?" said Herriot.

When we turned to follow the big yellow trucks, there were signs on the side road. Lake Gertrude, they said. The Lake Gertrude Pavilion, said others. Bide-Awee. Cozy Nook. Soft-drink signs were affixed to the tree trunks at the turn. They had been shot at, with No. 6 shot, by last year's sportsmen; and years before.

"Gertrude!" I said, as we turned to follow the big yellow trucks.

Their dust was still hanging.

"Why," I cried, "Lake Gertrude has never had a trout in it in its life! Sunfish. Chub."

Herriot followed on.

"Gertrude!" I protested. "There's been summer cottages on it for 50 years! It's a great big tourist lake, with hotels and motels and juke boxes."

Herriot kept right on.

The last approach to Lake Gertrude is down a steep hill.

At the crest of it, Herriot drew off to park on the side of the road.

Below us, the three tank trucks had pulled up beside a large wharf, the main access to Lake Gertrude. Moored to the wharf were three aircraft—two bright yellow Beavers of the Department of Lands and Forests: and a larger one, not yellow; a Norseman, the workhorse of the north.

At least 20 men were already swarming around the tank trucks.

"Oh, Lord!" said Herriot.

As we watched, the men were unloading the tanks from the trucks, putting them on dollies and hand trucks and wheeling them expertly up gangplanks into the aircraft.

"What do you say?" I suggested.

So Herriot drove on down the hill to the wharf, and we got out. There were three or four Lands and Forests men in their brown uniforms.

"Doing a planting job?" I asked, cheerfully.

"Yep."

"Are they going far?"

"A couple of hundred miles," said the Lands and Forests man. "Up north."

"Ah, yes," said I.

We watched the aircraft loaded with the tanks and their little oxygen attachments.

"Let's go," suggested Herriot.

"Let's wave them off," I countered.

So we waited, and saw the three aircraft taxi out into Lake Gertrude, with all her sunfish and mud-cats, and roar away into the blue.

The great thing about trout fishing, it is unpredictable.

The Nose

The luckiest find a man can make is a little old run-down village hotel.

It is far off the highways, lost down maybe 20 miles of gravel road. Red brick, there it stands in slow decay, its driving sheds long since fallen away, some of its windows boarded up. The village nestling around it is 11 cottages. The population is 80.

Eighty, including the village school teacher and the barber, both of whom have rooms in the old hotel. Three or four other rooms are occupied by the present owner of the place, to whom it came by a long and half-forgotten succession of misfortunes. It is, of course, no longer a hotel. It is just an overlarge place where quiet people dwell. Most of its rooms are abandoned. The back regions of the hotel are cluttered with ancient junk and full of plaster dust.

171

But . . . ! But, 400 yards down the village street, under a bridge on the gravel road, runs a stream. A limpid, full, gin-clear stream. And the stream is full of trout. And the farmer who owns it is willing to lease it for a year, five years, 10 years. Name your own figure.

We found such a hotel. There were eight of us in the party. We leased the stream. We begged the man who owned the old place to persuade his wife to give us breakfast and supper. Then we, having won their hearts with our jovial goodwill, per-suaded them to fix up two or three of the aban-doned rooms for us; nothing fancy, mind, just any old thing where we could sleep.

And presto! We had a treasure. In one year, it was a glory in our lives. We came up, starting May 1, every Friday evening and stayed to Sunday after tea. The rooms got better and better; the meals were real country. Our cars were always parked out front. Strangers passing by began to drop in for a meal.

We looked down our noses at strangers.

The second year, some strangers came and fished the stretch of stream next down from our leased piece. They wanted rooms. There were none. We had them all. We looked down our noses at them. In the dining room, they sat at an extra table that was put in for them. We sat at our tables, talking, stiff and subdued.

One Friday evening, we arrived and found three strange cars parked in front.

Strangers to the number of six or seven were cheerfully inhabiting the place.

"You haven't let them our rooms?" we asked our host, scandalized.

"No, I fixed up a couple of extra rooms . . . "

The eight of us, by dark, were gathered in our rooms listening, with growing horror, to the merry sounds of strange company in the house.

A piano began to sound downstairs. Tinny, and a little flat, it tinkled through the old hotel. We heard some fine, sweeping chords nonetheless, and a voice began to sing Joyce Kilmer's *Trees*.

It was a good voice.

We went to the head of the stairs quietly and listened down.

A couple of us quietly went downstairs, to see them clustered singing around the old piano.

That is how we met the Dutchmen. They were a gang from the Kitchener-Waterloo country of Ontario.

They leased the stretch upstream from ours, and our host cleaned up four or five more of the old abandoned rooms. And now there were six tables in the dining room, at which we and the Dutchmen sat together, at random, and looked down all our noses at strangers who dropped in.

Ah, they were company, those Dutchmen. They brought beer in small barrels, and pigs' tails in pails and home-made bread of a character undreamed of by us un-Dutch. Cheese, too, strange, hair-raising cheese. And knackwurst and weird bolognas.

Sunday mornings, we all had breakfast together as a matter of convenience for the host and his family going to church. We were, of course, by Sunday, unshaven and a little unkempt, as becomes trout fishermen.

When we straggled into the dining room, two strangers sat at one of our tables, eating breakfast. They were young and very stylish. Their car outside was an English sports car, red. The girl I recognized as the daughter of a very wealthy family in my city, and the man I learned later was a master at a private school for boys.

They sat looking down their noses. They looked down their noses at the bacon and eggs, the toast, the homely marmalade in the saucer. They held their water glasses up to the light to see if they were clean. They wiped their knives and forks on their paper table napkins.

But mostly they looked down their noses at us, as we filed ungainly in for our happy breakfast. They looked boldly down their noses at us, as only the sports-car type can. They muttered amusing things to each other, laughed briefly, smiled arctically. We tried, but could not look down our noses at them. They outsnooted us. They were professional. At their table, they murmured. At our tables, now a little crowded, we muttered.

Suddenly, Fred Krug, the king of the Dutchmen, who ran a stammering school in Kitchener and sang *Trees* and played the beat-up old piano, rose and left the room. He went upstairs. He returned in a moment and went out the screen doors to the front of the hotel.

Then he returned and sat down, a look of splendor on his face.

In a few moments, the sports-car drivers got up and left, with sweeping airs.

"Boy!" we said, as we heard their car depart. "Did they ever look down their noses . . . "

"They will in a minute or two," said Fred Krug triumphantly, "as soon as their exhaust manifold warms up. I lifted the hood of their car and put a nice piece, about the size of a cigarette package, on their manifold."

"A piece of what?" we cried.

"Limburger, what else?" said Fred.

The Poachers

Skipper Howard telephoned me in crisp excitement.

"How," he asked, "would you like to come poaching?"

"Poaching!" I protested.

"Yes," said Skipper. "Trout. Speckled trout."

Skipper, of all people! The last man in the world to go poaching. Why, he owns one of the loveliest leases on a trout stream in the whole province. He also belongs to two private fishing clubs. He HATES poachers.

I gave the telephone transmitter a shake.

"Skipper, is that you?" I asked clearly.

"Yes, sir," said Skipper. "I'm going tomorrow morning at 7 o'clock. Baldy McClemon is picking me up. And I want you to come."

"Baldy," I squalled, "McClemon!"

For Baldy McClemon is the one man Skipper would never go fishing with under ANY circumstances, much less poaching. Baldy is a fish hog. He isn't interested in fishing. He is only interested in fish. His idea of fishing is to fill his creel with the biggest fish he can catch, by any means whatever, and beat everybody else. He thinks fishing is a competition.

"You're kidding!" I accused.

"No, sir, it's a fact," stated Skipper in a grim sort of voice. "I'm going poaching. Baldy was in here not 10 minutes ago. He tells me he has located the loveliest little bit of river he ever fished. Full of trout. Beautiful trout, a pound, pound and a half. But it's posted. Private water."

"Whereabouts?" I inquired, still incredulous.

"On the Beaver River," said Skipper.

"That's where your lease is," said I. "Anywhere near your piece?"

"I think," said Skipper, "it IS my piece!"

"Aw, no!"

"Yep," said Skipper. "He described exactly my lease. He says you go in on the fourth concession. The end of the stream is all thickly wooded with cedar. Then you work your way upstream, and come to a bend, where the open fields begin. And up at the far end is a little cottage . . ."

"Skipper!"

"Will you come?" he demanded. "Poaching?"

I was at Skipper's house by 6:30 a.m. and we had breakfast.

Baldy McClemon arrived in his Cadillac at 7 sharp.

When he saw me come out with Skipper, in our fishing togs and carrying our tackle, Baldy was a little taken aback. He does not care for me.

"Aw, Skipper," he protested, "I don't think there will be room for the three of us on the stream, under the circumstances."

But Skipper said it was too late to turn me down. He supposed it wouldn't hurt to let me in on the deal.

It is about two hours' drive to the Beaver. Ah, what a stream, and what a lovely mile of it Skipper had leased! It is his love, his life, his treasure. It is the sort of possession you would as soon share with your friends as you would your sweetheart. Skipper guards it at some expense. He bought five acres of the farm, along the stream, when he made the 20-year lease of the fishing; and on the five acres he built a little cottage. He employs an elderly couple to live in the cottage, to guard the stream, to grow a market garden, and to put him up for meals and a bed whenever he visits his paradise.

"We'll have to be pretty careful," warned Baldy McClemon, as we rode smooth and fast up the highway. "There's an old man lives in that cottage I was telling you about, Skipper. He comes snooping along every little while. Nearly caught me the last couple of times I've been up."

"How will we wiggle out of it," asked Skipper, "in case he does catch us?"

"I carry a letter in my pocket," explained Baldy. "It is from an imaginary person, giving me permission to fish on an imaginary stream. Whenever I get caught on any of these private waters, I always produce the letter. And when the guy who catches me tells me I am not on that water, I am very astonished, and very apologetic, and tell him I thought I had followed most carefully the directions on how to reach the right place. It always works."

"Why don't you," asked Skipper, "with all your money, Baldy, get a place of your own? Why don't you lease some stream? It would be less risky."

"Aw, it's too much trouble owning a place," said Baldy. "You are always chasing poachers. Besides, it's a waste of money. Especially when you can find spots like this one we're going to. The guy who owns it apparently never comes up except on weekends. So we're safe enough, in the middle of the week."

Skipper gave me the wink as we went onto the side roads, and sure enough came to the bottom end of his lease.

Baldy wouldn't let us out at the stream. He parked and carefully locked his de luxe big car a

quarter of a mile down the side road, in an incon-
spicuous lane.

"Got to be cagey!" he explained, gleefully. "It
doesn't pay to leave your car too near where you
are operating. I can teach you boys a few tricks!"

Then he led us through the woodlots, and can-
nily over some fields, low down, until we reached
the stream.

We had better than two hours to fish before
noon.

"I'll lead," said Baldy, "in case I meet anybody;
and I can give you warning. You follow along, and
catch up to me by noon. I'll be up toward the cottage by then, and be lookout. Good luck!"

"O.K.," agreed Skipper and I hoarsely.

It was painful for Skipper to see Baldy fishing
ahead of him up the beautiful little river. Baldy had
his usual luck. He fished flies for a while and then
put on worms. Later, he put on trout fins and bits
of trout flesh.

As we rounded bends and saw him playing his
trout and sliding them, big, chunky trout, like a
fishmonger into his creel, Skipper would groan.
But the groans ended in chuckles.

We got a few nice trout each, even though Baldy
had looted the pools and stickles ahead of us.

Just at noon, we overtook him, sitting on the
bank awaiting us.

"Take it easy," he warned. "Scrunch down. Come
up here beside me. The old woman is coming along
the far bank."

"What'll we do?" hissed Skipper and I, in terror.

"Leave it to me," said Baldy. "I'll pull the letter
on her. I'll show you boys how it's done."

An elderly woman, her hands full of trilliums
and dog-tooth violets, appeared on the far bank,

coming along the path. When she saw us, she came forward.

"Hello, Mr. Howard," she called across. "Have you got sandwiches with you; or will you be coming to the cottage for lunch?"

"Two of us will be coming to the cottage," called Skipper. "Did my car arrive?"

"Yes, the boy brought it an hour ago," said the housekeeper. "He's at the cottage now."

"Good," said Skipper. "Mr. McClemon will be going home in his own car."

Baldy stood up. He never said a word.

"You keep your fish, Baldy," said Skipper.

And Skipper and I waded across and joined the housekeeper and walked along the path to the cottage, and didn't even look back.

The Frying Pan

It is sometimes necessary to get even with people. If my guide's name had been Joe, I don't think I would have bothered about getting even. But his name was Christophe Berriatreault dit St. Louis. We are old, long-time friends now; so he won't mind me telling about getting even.

After a long, long wait, I finally got elected to a very exclusive fishing club in the Laurentians. A new member of such a club is always the object of considerable scrutiny by his seniors. The club guides do a little scrutinizing, too. None of them wants to be drawn as guide to a new member, for many reasons. But on the opening night of the season, 20 members were present at the club. The draw for guides was held. And I drew Christophe Berriatreault dit St. Louis.

It was an unpopular win. For Christophe was by long odds the prize guide of the club. Some of the old members congratulated me. Others were plainly disappointed that they hadn't got Christophe, especially some of the old, rich members. Christophe was openly disgusted.

He made no effort to hide his feelings. He wanted one of the rich old members himself. Their generosity was well known. Who could tell what sort of a skinflint I might turn out to be? New members are always a risk. Christophe muttered and growled among his fellow-guides. He sat on the steps of the guides' bungalow after supper, surrounded by his colleagues, switching black flies and mosquitoes with a small branch, accepting their condolences, staring at the ground. Maudit! The new member!

Next morning, a party of six members, one to a canoe, were to fish the lake in front of the clubhouse. We assembled at the log wharf, and Christophe got my canoe readied for me. He was very polite, very stiff.

"Christophe," I said politely, "would you get me a frying pan, please?"

"We do not require a frying pan," said Christophe. "We are all returning to the club for lunch."

"It is not for lunch," I explained, kindly. "I always like to have a frying pan in my canoe. Will you get one, please, a twelve-inch one?"

Christophe glanced meaningly around at the other members and the guides, shrugged his shoulders, raised his eyebrows, and swaggered back up to the clubhouse with every ounce of his body expressing disgust, grief, despair. New member?

Lunatic! That this should happen to him . . .

He brought the frying pan and handed it to me with mock courtesy, the eyes of the other guides and members on us with varying shades of amusement and curiosity. I stuck the frying pan up under the bow of the canoe, behind me. I sat in, facing the stony-eyed Christophe, and got my fly rod ready.

Now, I am not a great fly fisher, nor even a particularly good one. But I am a tremendously lucky one. It may be I have loved fly fishing so ardently and so long, it likes me in return. Such things may be. But for the purposes of my revenge, I needed a good trout and needed it soon.

The six canoes started down the lake, along the spruce-and-cedar shore. We were in procession, I third. Most of us members were casting along the shore, to get our casting arms limbered up. We were not expecting fish until we got a mile or so down the lake, to a well-known shore of boulders and spring holes.

But hardly 100 yards had we gone before one of my casts was taken by a trout, a speckled trout of at least three solid pounds. There was tremendous excitement as he boiled to the surface. My five fellow-members circled around, ceased fishing, to watch the battle. There were cheers for the new member and his first fish, a beauty.

Christophe was looking at me with a much friendlier eye as he manoeuvred the canoe. Finally, he got the net ready. I led the beautiful fish into it. He lifted. Cheers.

"Please," I said to Christophe, and reached to him for the net. I also reached for the frying pan behind me. I removed the fly from the trout's lip and lifted the lovely fish from the net for the gathering to see. I laid the huge creature across the frying pan. It hung far over both edges.

I chucked the trout over the side into the lake.

Christophe very nearly leaped in after it. Consternation filled his face. He stared at me as if paralyzed.

"I only keep the ones that fit the frying pan," I explained to him. "Come on. Let's go!"

I figured Christophe would never forget me.

And he never has.

We have caught hundreds of trout together since, including some mighty big ones. Which we keep.

For Art's Sake

"I see," I said to Jim, "That there are several new art schools opening up in Toronto."

"Yes," said Jim, "in times of trouble, art comes to life. True art languishes during physical prosperity. Only when the world is ill do the artists make their sweet voices heard."

"Yet the fool artists," I put in, "ought to know their stuff wouldn't sell in hard times like these."

"What has selling got to do with it?" snorted Jimmie. "Artists are above money! Art is the voice of the spirit. Above the horrid din of prosperity the voice of the spirit cannot be heard. But when the factories stand still, you hear again the soft, sweet music of the poet, painter, and musician."

"Do you ever hanker after being a real artist, Jimmie?" I asked. "You know, with paint and canvas?"

Jimmie got a little red in the face, and after hesitating a moment or two, he opened a drawer in his desk and pulled out a wooden box about as big as a portable typewriter.

He opened it, and revealed a whole collection of tubes of artists' paints, like tooth paste, long-handled brushes, bottles of oil and of turpentine. And in the lid of the box, fastened in wooden nicks, three or four small plain canvas boards, ready for painting on.

"I bought this," said Jim, "to start sketching. I am going to take up art seriously. Art with a capital A. And what's more, when the Fall comes, I am going to attend art school again, and instead of studying cartooning in six lessons, I am going to take lessons in real painting from real painters."

"Cartoons in color?" I asked. "You mean, 'Birdseye Centre' in red, white and blue?"

"No, sir," said Jim solemnly. "You don't call cartoons art, do you? I'm going to be a real artist. I am going to paint landscapes."

"Can I have some of them after you've done with them?"

"Why not take up painting yourself?" asked Jim. "Who knows but in that scraggy and half-baked body of yours dwells the spirit of the artist, the dreamer, the seer, the visionary?"

"Do you think there might be some art in me?" I asked.

"All the greatest artists in the world's history were funny looking," said Jim. "I bet if you tried your hand with brush and colors, you might turn out to be one of the greatest landscapists in Canada. Think of being a recognized artist, a famous master!"

"I could wear a cape and a big slouch hat," I said.

"And grow whiskers," said Jim. "Listen. I was thinking just the other day that we waste a lot of time fishing. What do we get out of fishing? Just a day in the open air, in the sunshine and in contact with Mother Earth. There is nothing more to it. We don't care about the fish."

"My wife gave up cooking my fish six years ago," I admitted.

"Well then," cried Jim eagerly, "let's both take up sketching. You get a box of colors like this, and we can go out into Nature and get all the benefits of sunshine and fresh air, and instead of coming home with nothing, we will have a sketch, a painting; an enduring memento of our day in God's fresh air."

"Jimmie," I cried, "I believe you've got hold of something! Do you know, I was beginning to lose the kick in fishing."

"I'll get you the outfit," said Jim. "All you want is the sketching box. You don't need any easel. The back of the box is the easel and you sit on the ground or on a stump."

"Where would we go?" I asked.

"Where better than up to where we usually go fishing?" asked Jim. "There are spots there that are sacred to us, views and landscapes that are graven on our hearts. Let us start our artistic careers by fastening on canvas, for posterity, those scenes we have learned to love."

I was deeply moved. Jim has his great moments. And before the weekend, Jim had got me a little artist's sketching box just like his own. And we proceeded up to the lake where Jim and I have fished for years for pike and pickerel, taking hundreds of these homely fish on our fine light casting tackle.

"Should we take along a rod," I asked, "just to use during rest periods? You know, in case our fingers get cramped while we are painting? So we can stroll down and make a few casts."

"No," said Jim, "fishing is fishing and art is art. We are going to paint. Let's paint."

So for the first time in nearly twenty years, Jim and I drove up to the dear old lake without any fishing tackle. Up the highway, across the dear familiar gravel road, down through the beloved valley, out through little sweet countryside roads where we saw a hundred beautiful things to paint, quaint farms, colorful old barns, hills, elm trees— mile by mile we drove through the country, with our brand new sketching boxes dancing on the back seat of the car where for so many years had ridden the clattering tackle boxes, the rods, nets, rubber boots and raincoats.

It was a glorious hour when we reached the shores of the lake. The spring afternoon was waning. The water was still and blue. We parked the car in the old familiar grove of pines, and with our sketching boxes in our eager hands, we strolled down to the water's edge.

"I think I'll walk along to the gravel bar," I said to Jimmie. "There is where my sweetest memories linger. That little bay, with pine-clad walls, the far shore shimmering in the sunlight, the shadows on the near shores, the water limpid and blue above the gravel bar."

"I was thinking of going there myself," said Jim. "Why not let us both start there. We have about three hours to paint."

"And you can give me the lessons you promised," I said. "We can sit together."

"I don't remember much from my student days," said Jim, "but you're welcome to what I can tell you. Just a few things about mixing your colors and so forth."

We strolled through the woods, remarking the beautiful landscapes, the far shore dim and color-ful, the near shores dark and filled with blues, mauves, greens and browns.

"You see," said Jim as we walked, "you squeeze a little of each color around the edge of the palette which is in your box. Then you outline the land-scape, getting its general proportions, with a faint trace of whatever color you will eventually put in. These near shores you outline with brown. The far shores with blue, and the sky you smear in with light blue."

"Smear?" "Well, you see," said Jim, "the beauty of painting with oil colors is that you can cover up mistakes with another color. You can lighten it or darken it. Painting isn't like plumbing or carpentry. You don't have to paint it as it really is, and you can shift it around a lot, with a dab here and a dab there."

We came to the gravel bar.

There were the old familiar boulders where for half a lifetime we had sat, amidst which we had stood to cast far out over the sunken gravel shoals for pike and pickerel, amongst which our shouts had echoed as we struck and played the monster fish of bygone years. There lay the lunch boulder, on whose flat surface we had always laid out our sandwiches and tomatoes. There was the famous Billy boulder, around which Billy had snubbed his line the time he hooked the monster pike.

What a spectacle of beauty! What a thing to paint! An artist could not paint that lovely scene, the bay, the towering shore, the blue water, shading from black to sheerest sky blue, without conveying a message of joy and promise to all beholders.

"A man couldn't look at that picture," I said to Jimmie, "without knowing that a big fish was likely to rise any minute in the middle of it."

"It's a glorious bit of land and water scape," agreed Jim, slowly walking this way and that to get a good view of the scene.

"We have to work out the composition," said Jim. "We have to decide what we are going to put into the picture and what to leave out."

He strolled back and forwards, holding his hands up to his face like blinkers, to frame off certain parts of the view.

"Here," he said. "We'll sit here. We will paint from that white birch tree on that point right across to the far headland, taking in all this fore shore, the boulders, the high bank there and the sand beach here."

So, with not a little trembling for so important an occasion—our first painting—we sat down side by side, and resting our artists' boxes on our knees, we undid the latches and opened them up.

The white canvas square seemed rather terribly empty at first. Jim squeezed bits of different colors on the small board palette, and I did likewise. Then Jim took a small brush, and, using brown paint, he outlined the far point, the shape of the boulders in front of us, and I did likewise. By watching where Jim placed these lines on his canvas, I got a fair start.

Then Jim took another bigger brush and with bold, sweeping strokes, he laid on pale blue for both sky and water. My blue was deeper, and, if I may say so, prettier than Jim's.

He washed out the brush in turpentine and took up a dab of brown paint and with a wiggling, staggering wrist movement, he started to make light and dark, big and small, heavy and light touches of brown all over the far and near points.

I got mine a little too dark, and I could not manage that staggery wrist motion, so that more or less, my far shore appeared as a solid brown.

"I could make those rocks harder than they really are," I suggested. "I could make them a kind of granite shore, couldn't I?"

"Oh, sure," said Jim.

It was wonderful to watch him. But after he had been painting about fifteen or twenty minutes, during which time he was away ahead of me in the number of colors he had on, though not in the amount of paint, he began to groan softly to himself.

"What's the matter?" I asked.

"Oh, I'll never get that light, that golden light, the sun streaming from low down across that blue water! It can't be done," moaned Jimmie.

"Well, you've a long time to go yet," I said, "You don't expect a picture to be done in a few minutes."

"No," said Jim. "And that golden light won't last many minutes either."

I put a streak of bright yellow across where the sun shone, but it did not look right. Jim continued to groan. It was getting to be that witching hour, known to all fishermen, when what they call the "rise" is likely to commence. It is the loveliest hour in all art. Every time I see a painting of that time of day, that moment just when the sun strikes the tops of trees, I am filled with a deep, artistic longing. I don't know exactly whether it is a longing to paint or just a longing to go fishing.

I was resting my wrist, and Jim was softly moaning to himself as he touched colors skillfully on to the canvas, when suddenly, not forty yards from where we were sitting, right out opposite the Billy boulder where Billy had hooked the monster pike, there was a resounding splash!

Jim and I stopped and held our breath. We looked out at the big, widening ripples in the calm water of the gravel bar.

Jim turned his head and looked at me.

"Could you put that rise into the picture?" I asked, swallowing.

"Did you see him?" asked Jim huskily.

"No. I was watching you paint," I said.

"I bet he would go over ten pounds," said Jim.

We sat in hushed silence looking at the placid lake, the soft sunshine, the deepening shadows.

Jim sighed heavily, and leaned forward to his painting again. I got a good gob of mauve on my brush and began touching up the solid brown rocks, so as to give them a more fleshy, or more broken, life-like appearance.

Splash!

Right in the same spot!

Great big circular rings waving and bobbing, ever widening, as if a cocker spaniel dog had been dropped into the lake.

Jim laid down his brush. I closed my box and stood up.

"You really didn't bring any tackle?" asked Jim hopefully.

"You told me not to," I retorted.

"Well, I kind of thought you might sneak a rod in anyway," said Jim. "You can't count on some people at all."

We watched the silent water, the lucid shadows, the beauty. As we watched, there came another broad swirl over the gravel bar, a swirl as big as a wash tub, as some monster pike engulfed a minnow for his tea.

Suddenly Jim leaped up, scattering his artist's box in all directions.

"I forgot!" he shouted. "I have an old reel with a line on it in my tool box in the car!"

He started to run along the shore toward the far grove where the car was parked.

"Cut a rod," he shouted back to me. "I'll bring some wire to make line guides!"

While he was gone, I cut and trimmed a neat rod out of a birch sapling, a rod about six feet long, with a nice casting spring to it. Jim returned on the gallop, and between us we fastened the reel on to the butt of the birch gad and wound a couple of rings with wire for the line to run through. Out of his pocket book Jim drew two stout bass hooks.

"What for bait?" he asked anxiously, suddenly having forgotten that little detail.

I had not thought of it either. Meantime, regularly as a man dips his spoon into his soup, that big pike continued to roll, forty feet out on the gravel bar.

"Maybe I could find a worm or a salamander under these rotten logs," said Jim, energetically attacking the decayed wood.

But I had a better idea.

I cut another bit of birch about the size of a clothes peg. I trimmed it neatly, and with wire, I fastened Jim's two hooks to it. Then, sitting down with the artist's box on my knees, I took the little wooden peg and with red, green, blue and white paint I transformed it into a beautiful little wooden minnow.

Jim saw me and rushed over.

"Marvellous!" he cried.

We tied the wooden minnow, still wet, to the end

of the line. Jim, being the owner of the reel, had first cast.

He crept down to the edge of the water off the bar, and with a smooth, strong overhead swing cast the gallantly glittering minnow out to where the big pike had been disporting.

It splashed into the water. Jim started to reel it in, and it wobbled and struggled on the surface, like a minnow the big pike himself had injured.

There was a lazy roll and surge. Jim struck back with the birch gad. And the pike was on!

The peace was broken by our shouts and cries. The smooth placid water was threshed to a storm by the battling pike. The rocks were smeared with paint as we trod unheeding on the tubes of artist's colors strewn about.

But in due season, the big pike, eleven pounds of him, was drawn gasping on to the sand shore, and two exhausted artists fell down upon him and clasped his slimy length in their arms.